P9-CLZ-113

THE GREATEST DOT TO DOT ADVENTURE!

Adventure Book 2

By David Kalvitis

First Edition

monkeying around
www.monkeyingaround.com
Rochester, New York

Adventure Book 2

By David Kalvitis

First Edition

Copyright © 2014 by David R. Kalvitis
First Printing 2014
Printed in the United States of America

All rights reserved. No part of this book may be reproduced or transmitted in any form or by any means, electronic or mechanical, including photocopying, recording or by any information storage and retrieval system without written permission from the author. Contact the author for information, at the address below.

Monkeying Around
PO Box 10131
Rochester, New York 14610 USA
585-256-2660
800-553-4300
Fax: 585-442-2965
info@monkeyingaround.com
www.monkeyingaround.com

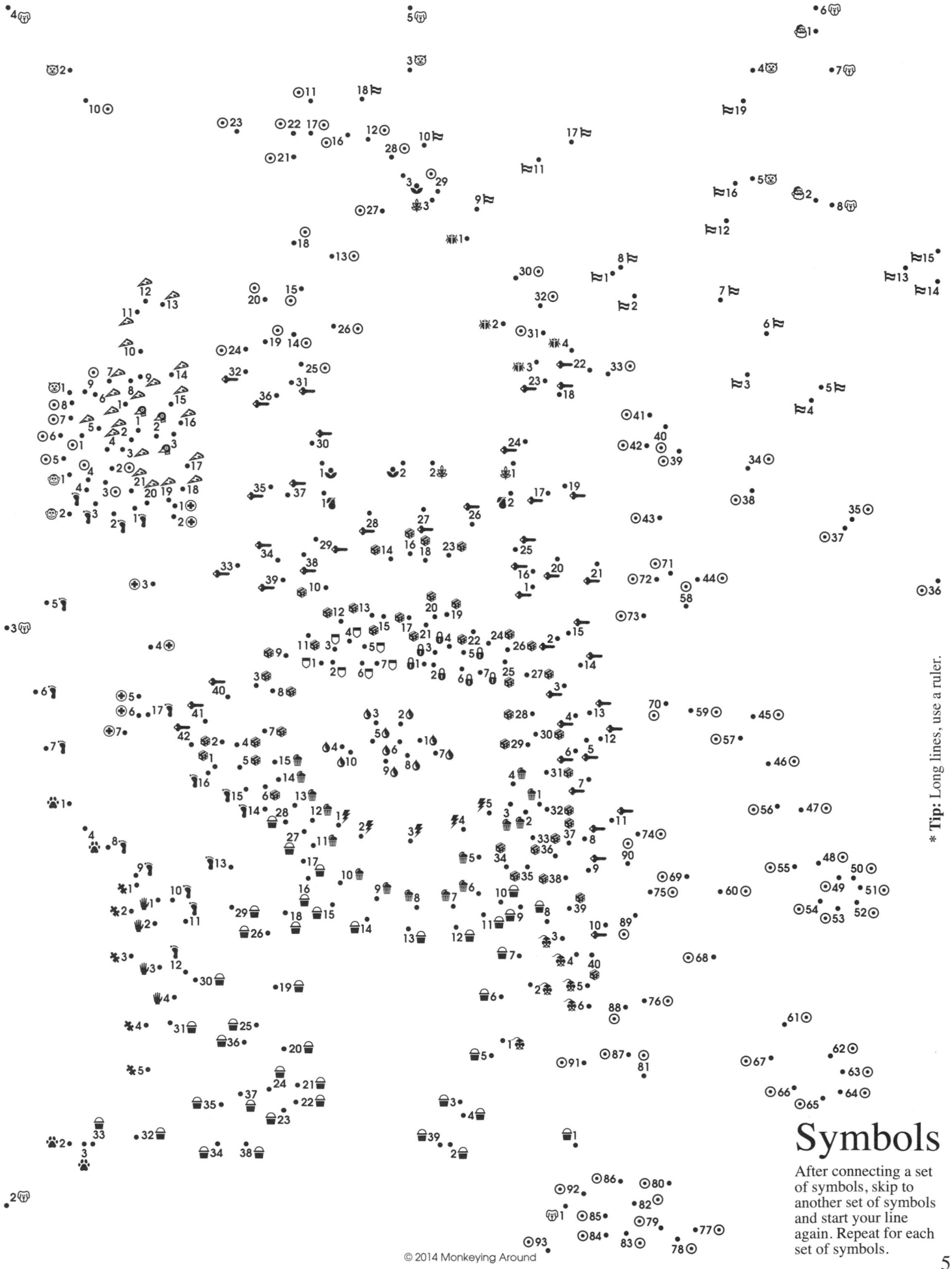

Symbols

After connecting a set of symbols, skip to another set of symbols and start your line again. Repeat for each set of symbols.

*** Tip:** Long lines, use a ruler.

© 2014 Monkeying Around

Stars

Stop at each star (★), then skip to the next number and start your line again.

End ★ 771

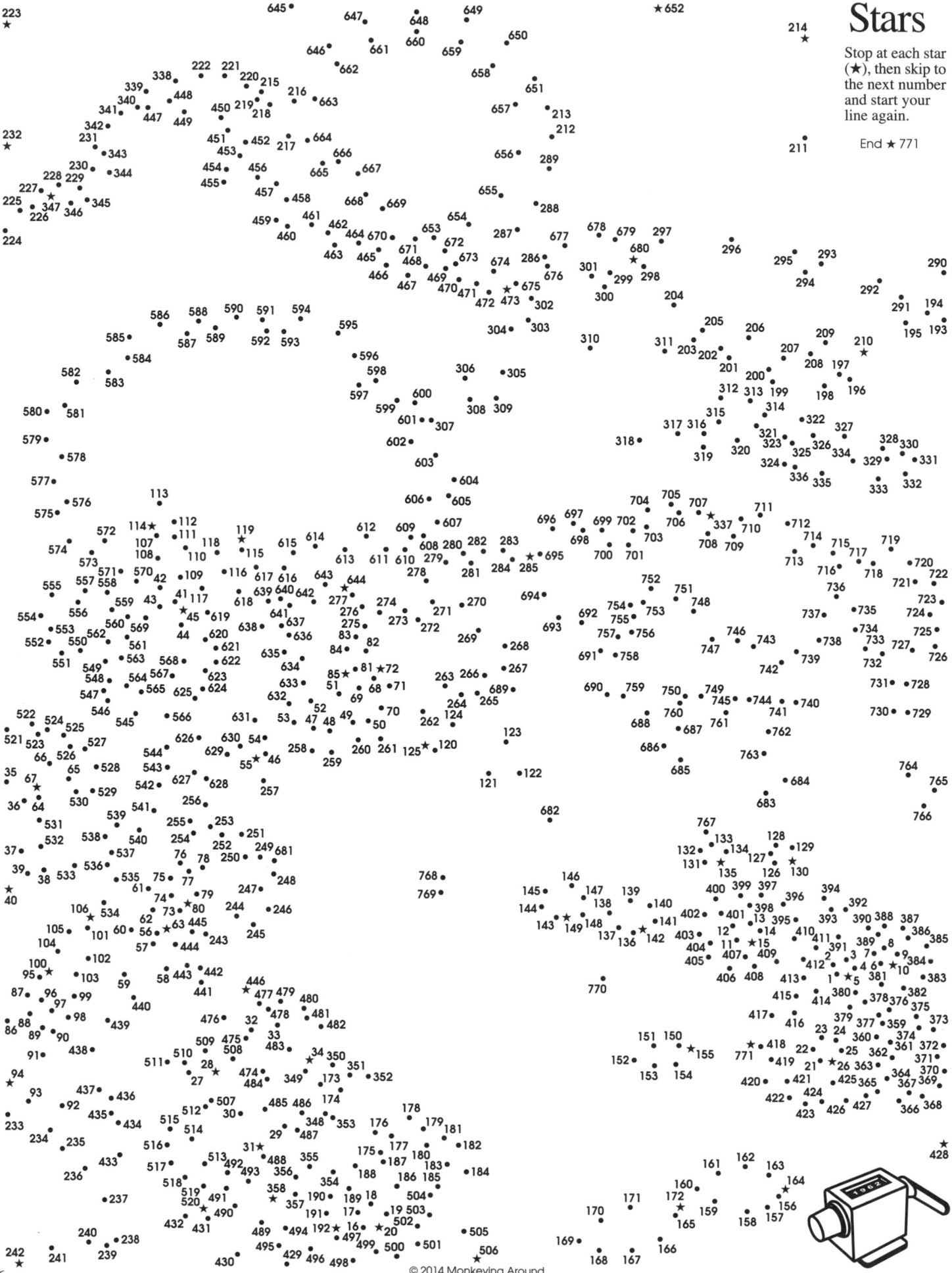

© 2014 Monkeying Around

Stars

Stop at each star (★), then skip to the next number and start your line again.

End ★ 434

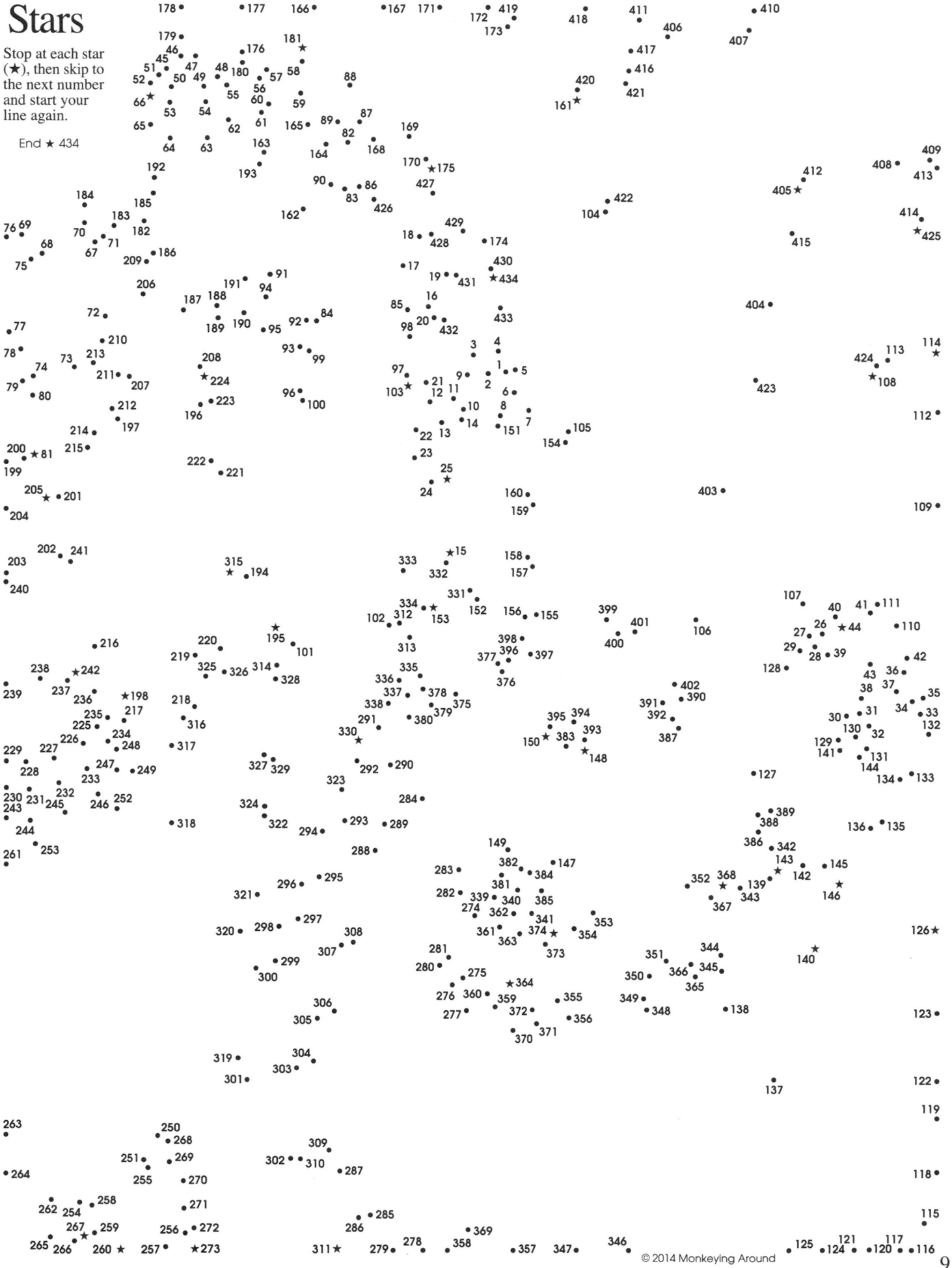

© 2014 Monkeying Around

Scene

Stop at each dog buscuit (🦴), then skip to the next number and start your line again.

End 🦴 507

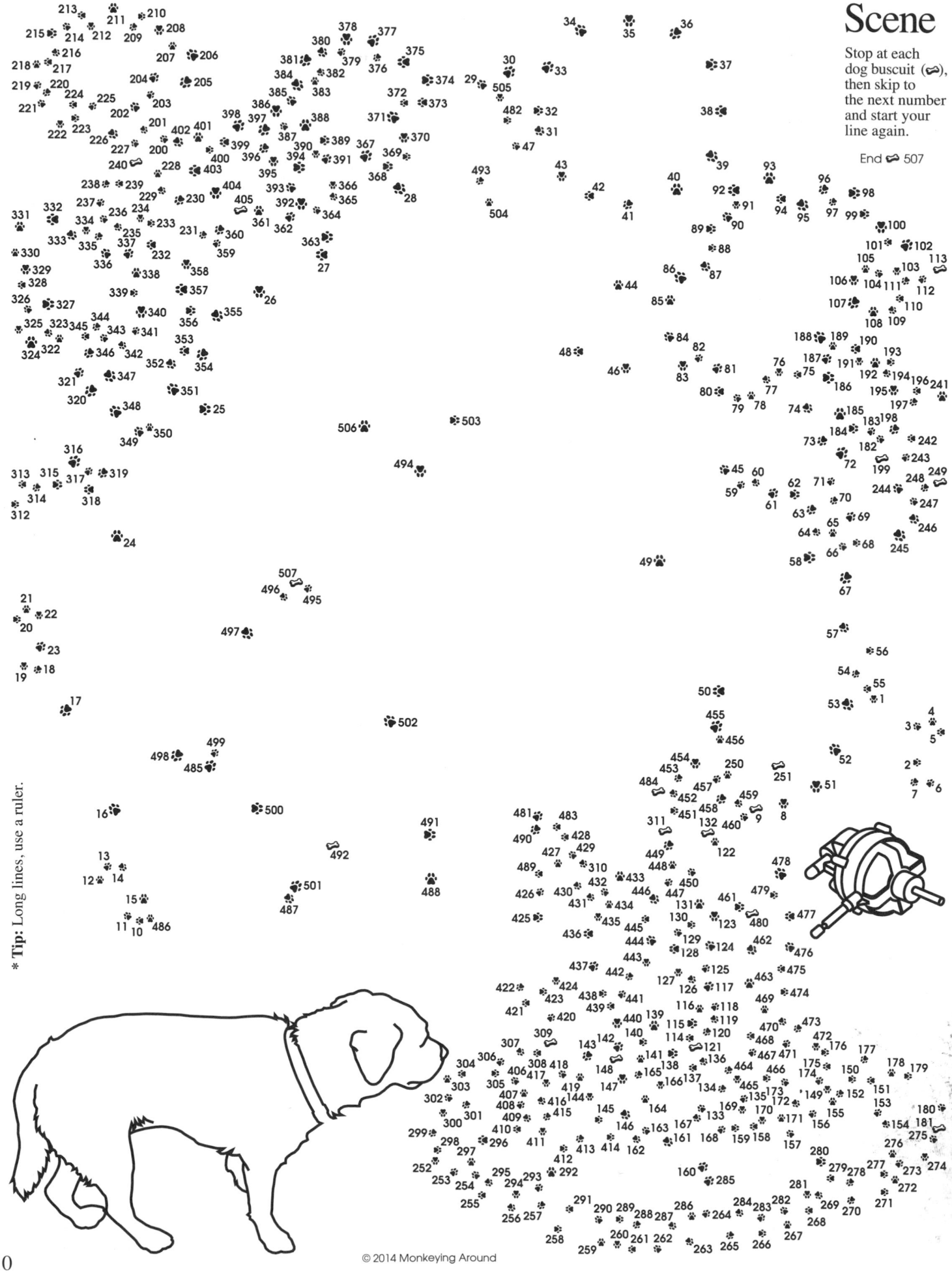

* **Tip:** Long lines, use a ruler.

© 2014 Monkeying Around

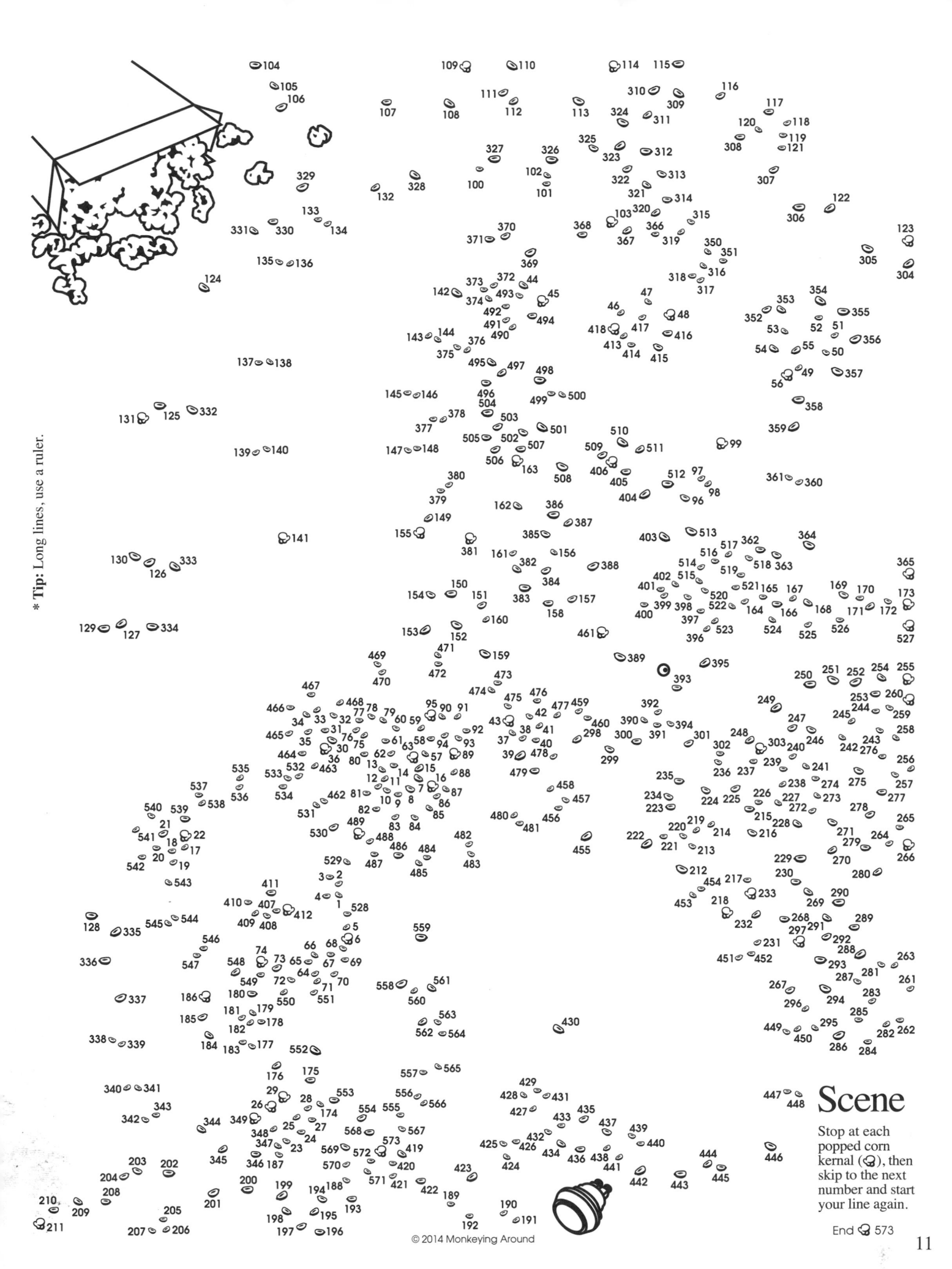

* **Tip:** Long lines, use a ruler.

Scene

Stop at each popped corn kernal (), then skip to the next number and start your line again.

End 573

© 2014 Monkeying Around

Odd/Even

Connect Dots:
odd numbers only
• 1 – 549
even numbers only
• 2 – 614

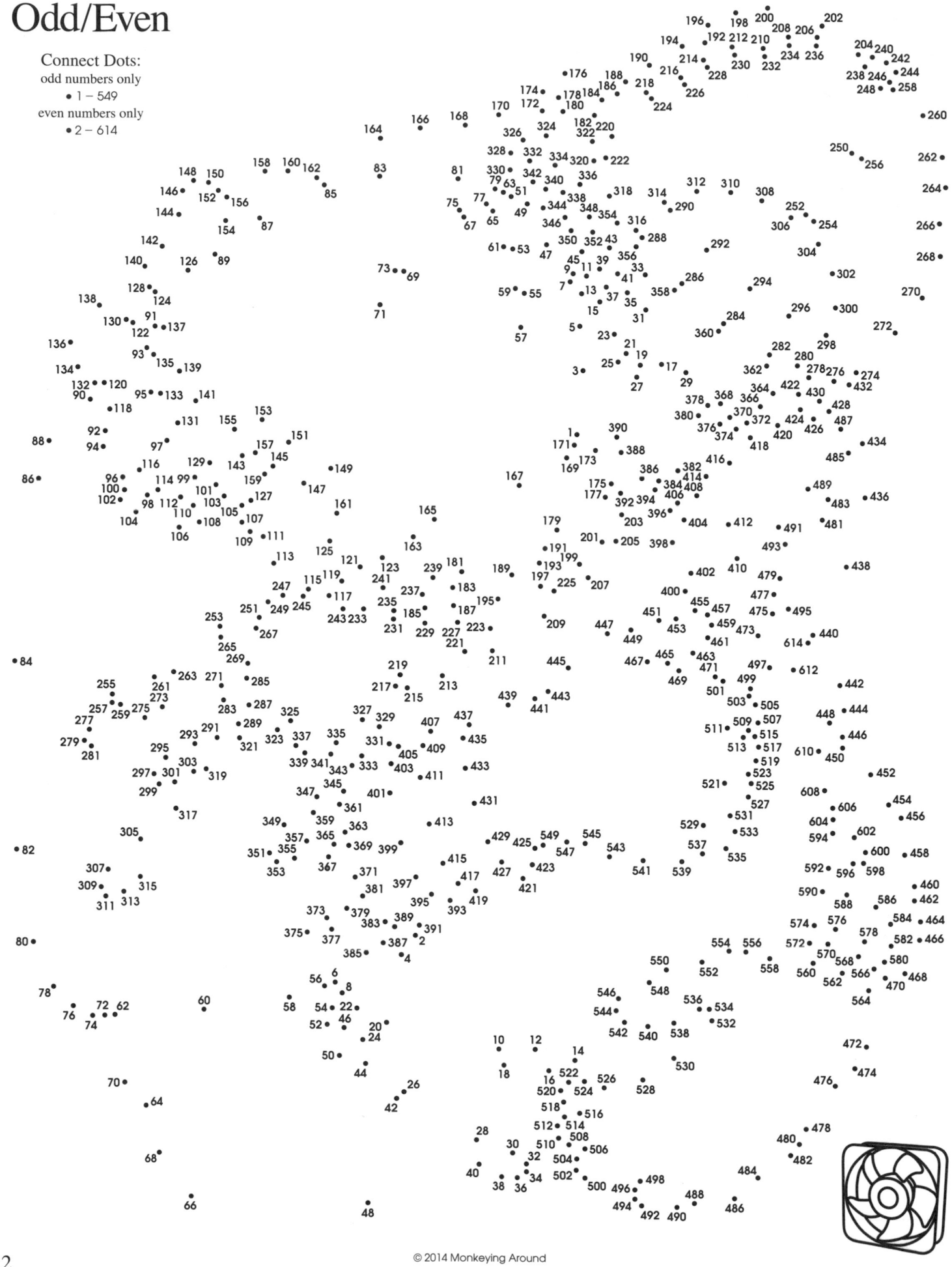

© 2014 Monkeying Around

Crazy Dots

Connect Dots:

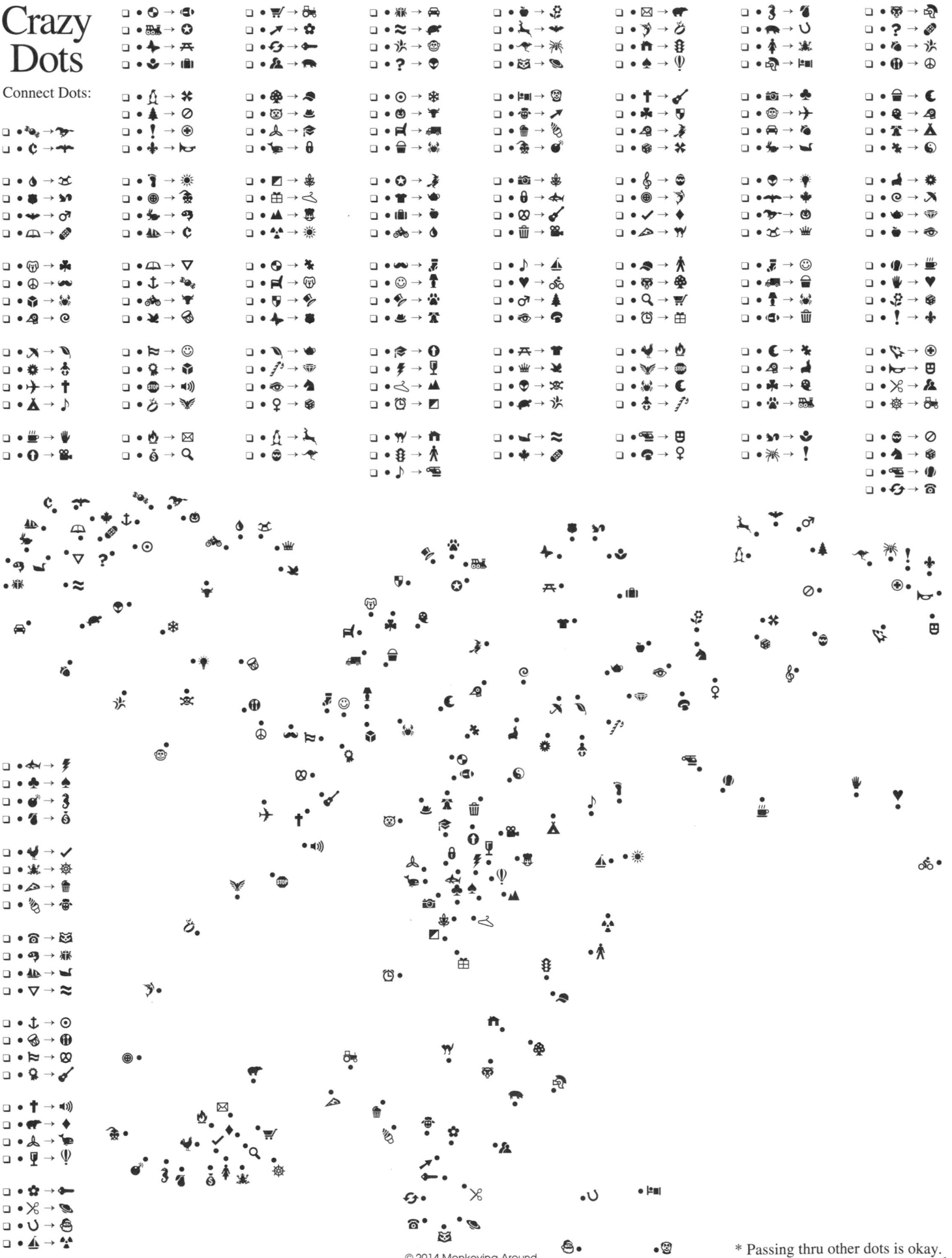

© 2014 Monkeying Around

* Passing thru other dots is okay.

2 Pages

Connect Numbers:

1 – 1287

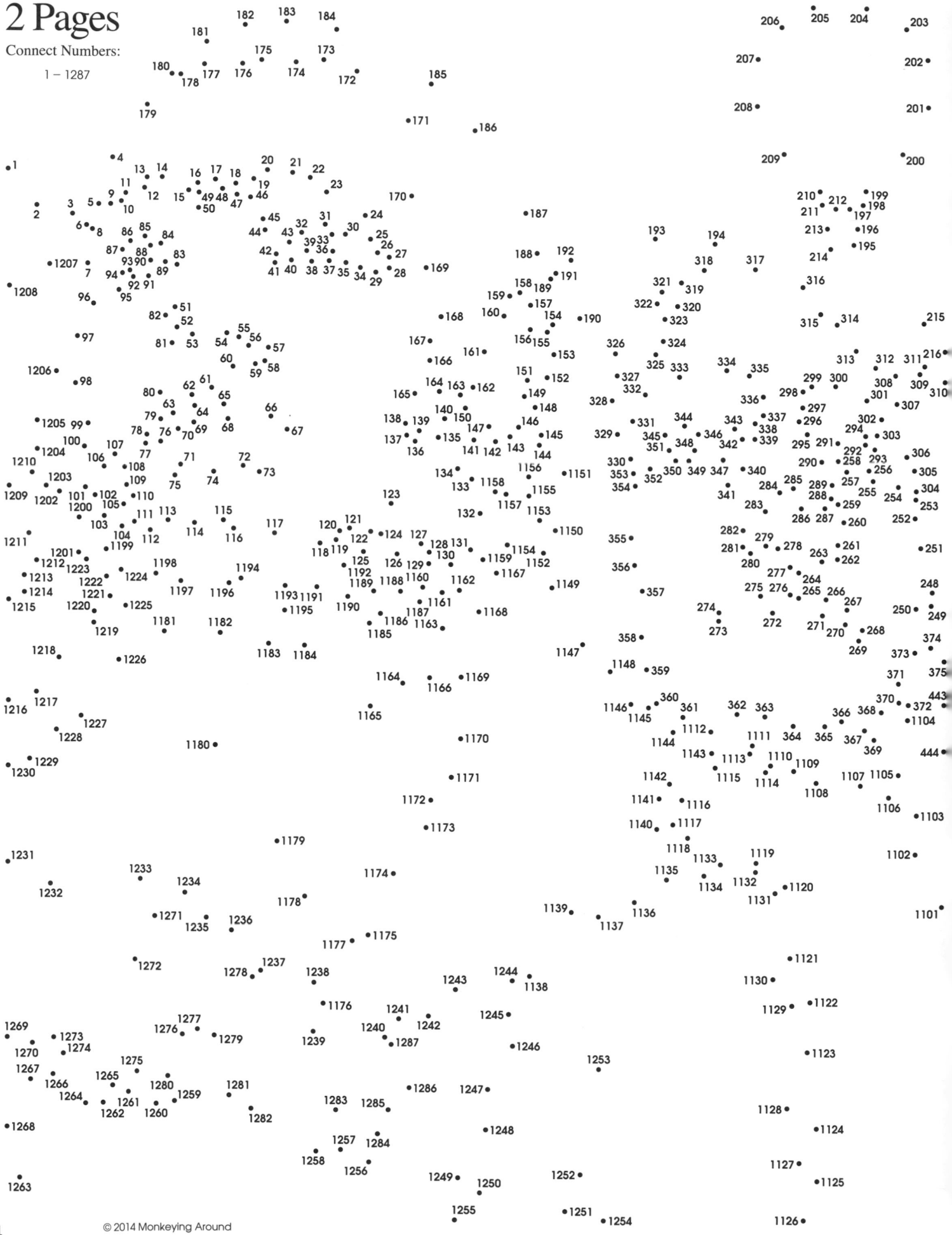

© 2014 Monkeying Around

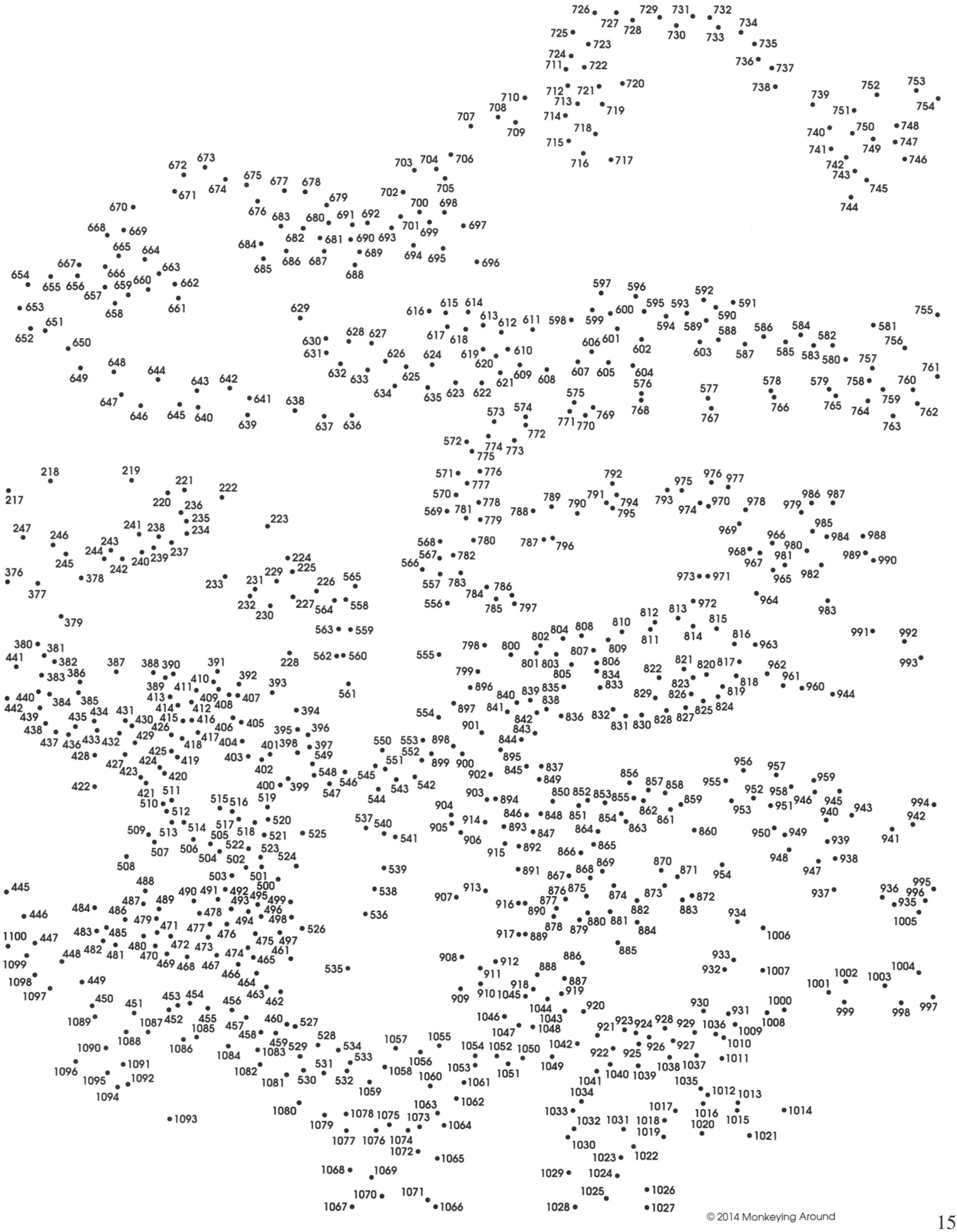

© 2014 Monkeying Around

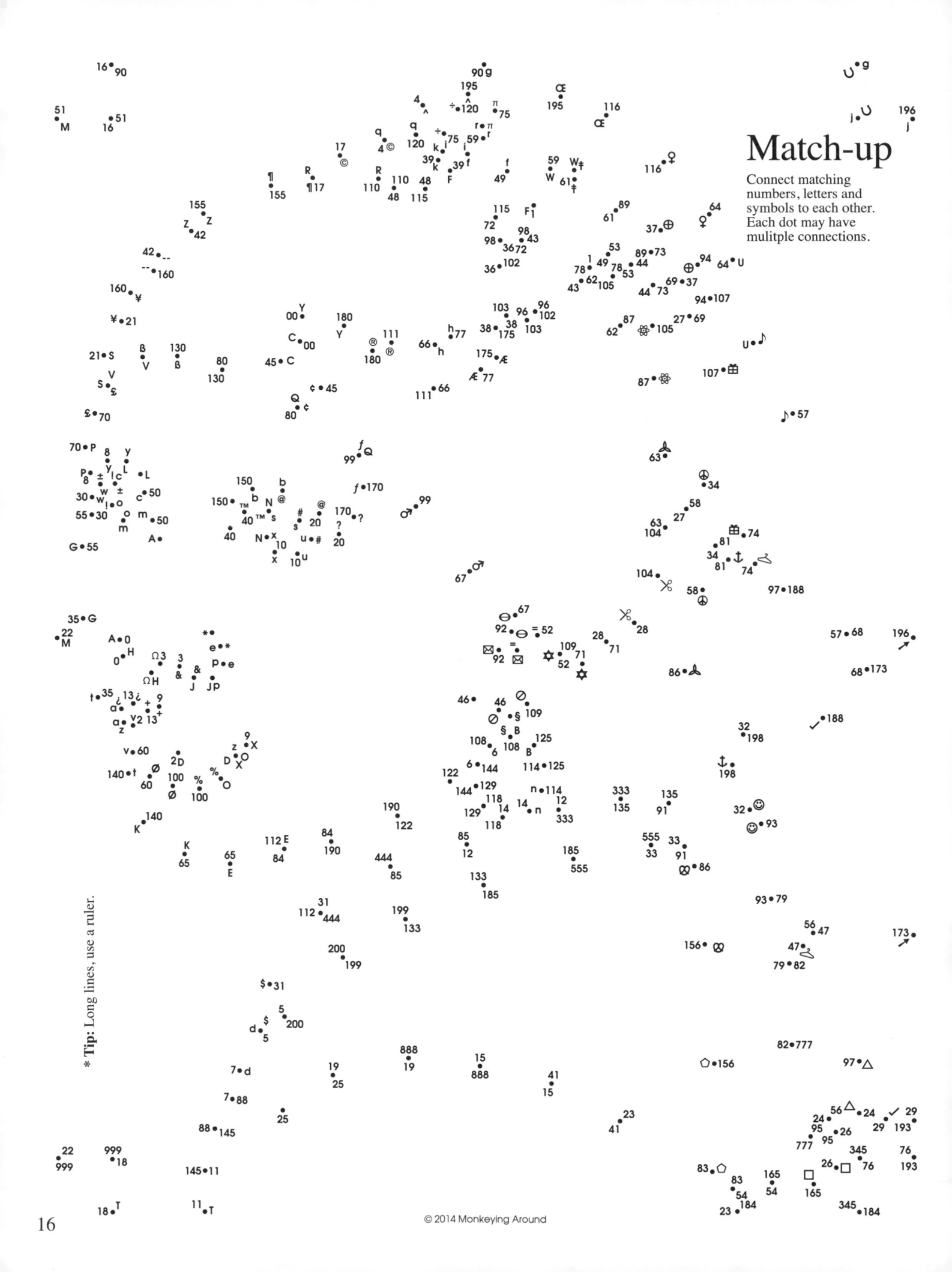

Match-up

Connect matching numbers, letters and symbols to each other. Each dot may have mulitple connections.

* **Tip:** Long lines, use a ruler.

© 2014 Monkeying Around

Stars

Stop at each star (★), then skip to the next number and start your line again.

End ★ 443

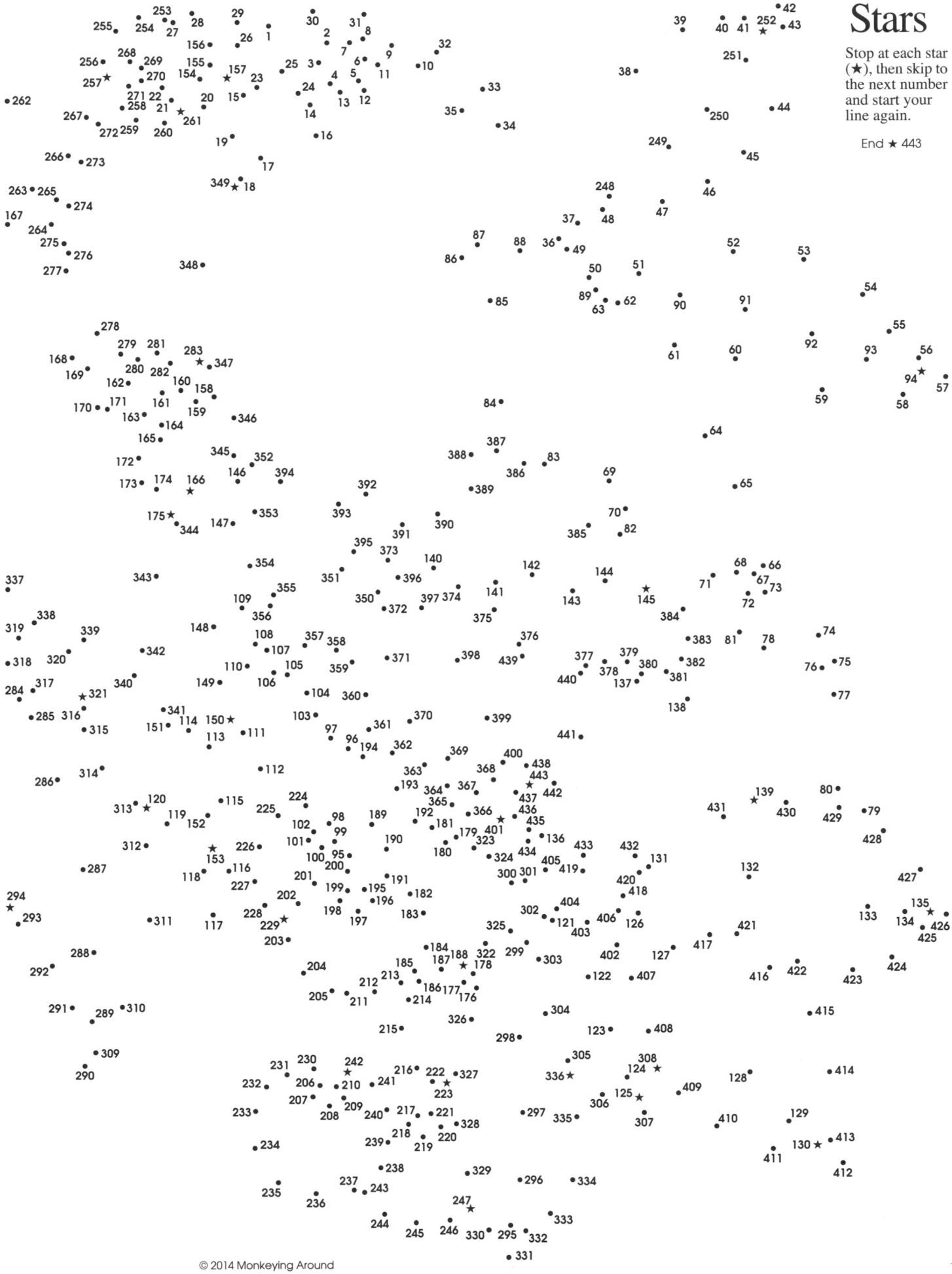

© 2014 Monkeying Around

Coordinates

Find the dot at each set of coordinates. Connect each dot to the next, making one continuous line. "x" numbers run up the side, "y" across the bottom. Use a corner of paper to make finding coordinates and dots easier.

x
y

Start Here!	x:30, y:26	x:03, y:33	x:04, y:35	x:05, y:35	x:17, y:31	x:18, y:32	x:16, y:34	x:28, y:37	x:30, y:38	x:28, y:56	x:29, y:56	x:30, y:55
x:15, y:34	x:14, y:33	x:13, y:33	x:17, y:37	x:18, y:37	x:16, y:35	x:19, y:33	x:34, y:32	x:32, y:34	x:32, y:39	x:37, y:47	x:39, y:45	x:36, y:50
x:20, y:34	x:21, y:34	x:18, y:31	x:20, y:30	x:21, y:32	x:23, y:32	x:22, y:30	x:40, y:52	x:38, y:51	x:40, y:47	x:39, y:50	x:41, y:50	x:42, y:49
x:21, y:30	x:28, y:28	x:30, y:28	x:30, y:36	x:28, y:35	x:29, y:35	x:29, y:34	x:47, y:44	x:47, y:43	x:46, y:42	x:38, y:38	x:38, y:39	x:40, y:42
x:26, y:32	x:25, y:30	x:24, y:30	x:27, y:35	x:28, y:36	x:27, y:36	x:21, y:35	x:35, y:33	x:35, y:31	x:33, y:28	x:50, y:40	x:50, y:38	x:49, y:37
x:31, y:40	x:31, y:28	x:32, y:28	x:32, y:30	x:33, y:30	x:34, y:31	x:42, y:48	x:41, y:46	x:43, y:43	x:42, y:41	x:44, y:43	x:33, y:27	x:33, y:26
x:32, y:48	x:32, y:49	x:34, y:52	x:41, y:54	x:41, y:53	x:40, y:44	x:39, y:44	x:33, y:37	x:33, y:35	x:46, y:09	x:45, y:08	x:44, y:08	x:32, y:25
x:31, y:25	x:19, y:00	x:18, y:02	x:18, y:03	x:30, y:25	x:24, y:19	x:22, y:20	x:20, y:25	x:19, y:26	x:18, y:26	x:15, y:25	x:12, y:22	x:16, y:23
x:18, y:25	x:19, y:25	x:16, y:22	x:14, y:21	x:13, y:19	x:13, y:16	x:16, y:17	x:21, y:21	x:21, y:20	x:16, y:16	x:14, y:15	x:15, y:14	x:18, y:15
x:23, y:18	x:19, y:15	x:14, y:13	x:12, y:13	x:10, y:16	x:10, y:17	x:13, y:21	x:12, y:21	x:10, y:18	x:09, y:18	x:10, y:22	x:11, y:24	x:10, y:26
x:09, y:26	x:08, y:25	x:08, y:24	x:09, y:24	x:08, y:23	x:07, y:24	x:07, y:25	x:11, y:30	x:12, y:30	x:10, y:27	x:12, y:25	x:15, y:29	End Here!

* **Tips:** Long lines, use ruler. Circling dots helps.

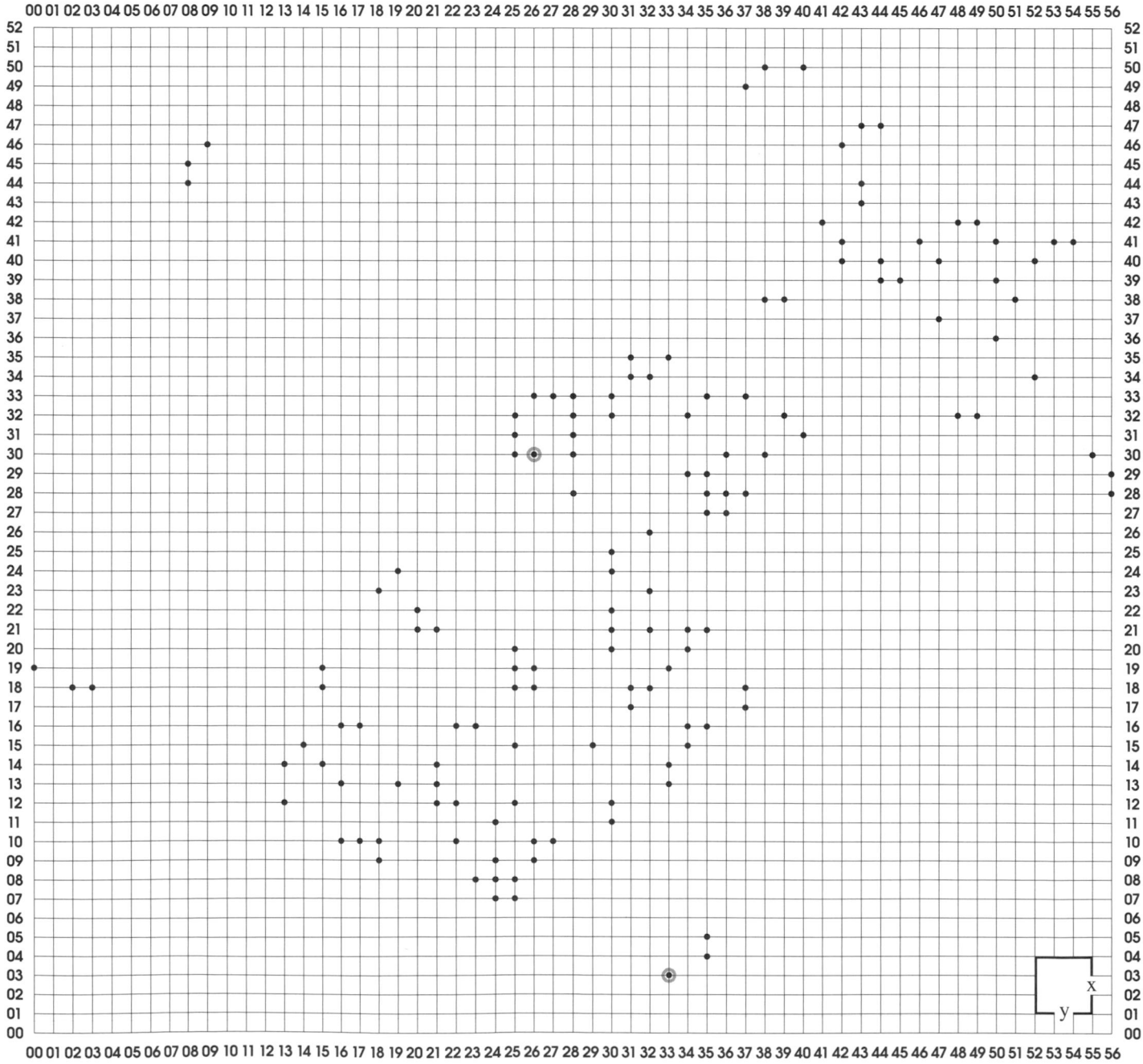

© 2014 Monkeying Around

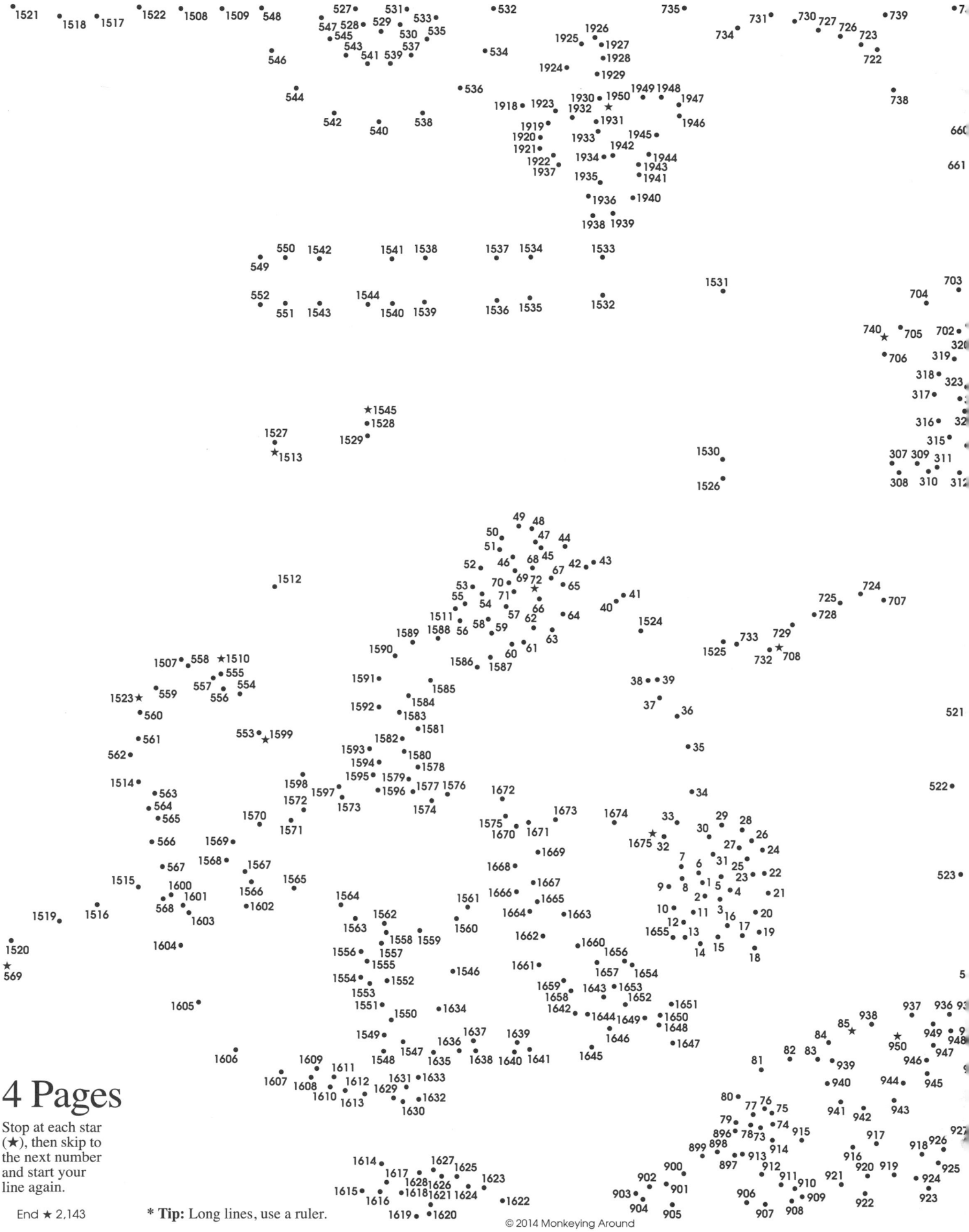

4 Pages

Stop at each star (★), then skip to the next number and start your line again.

End ★ 2,143

* **Tip:** Long lines, use a ruler.

© 2014 Monkeying Around

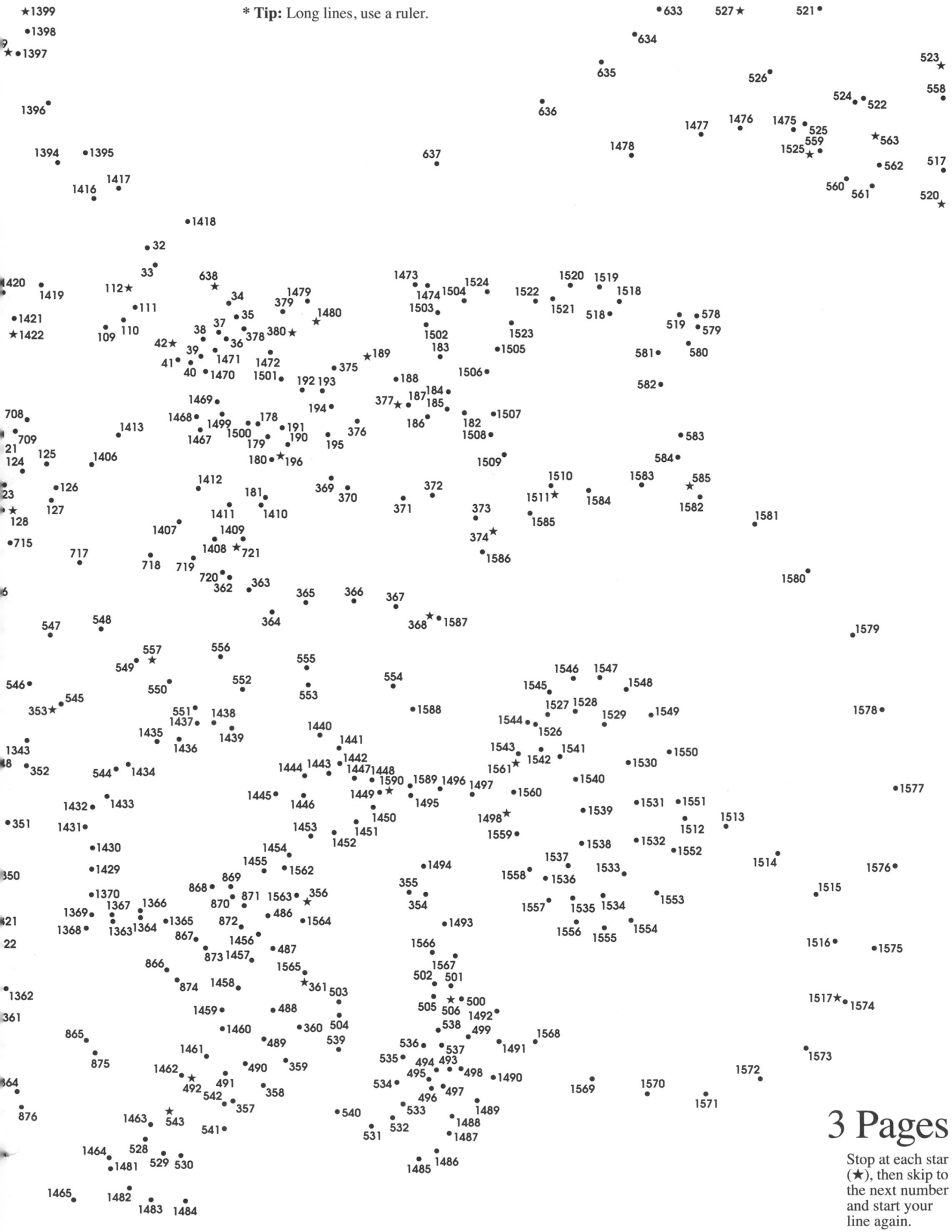

3 Pages

Stop at each star (★), then skip to the next number and start your line again.

End ★ 1590

© 2014 Monkeying Around

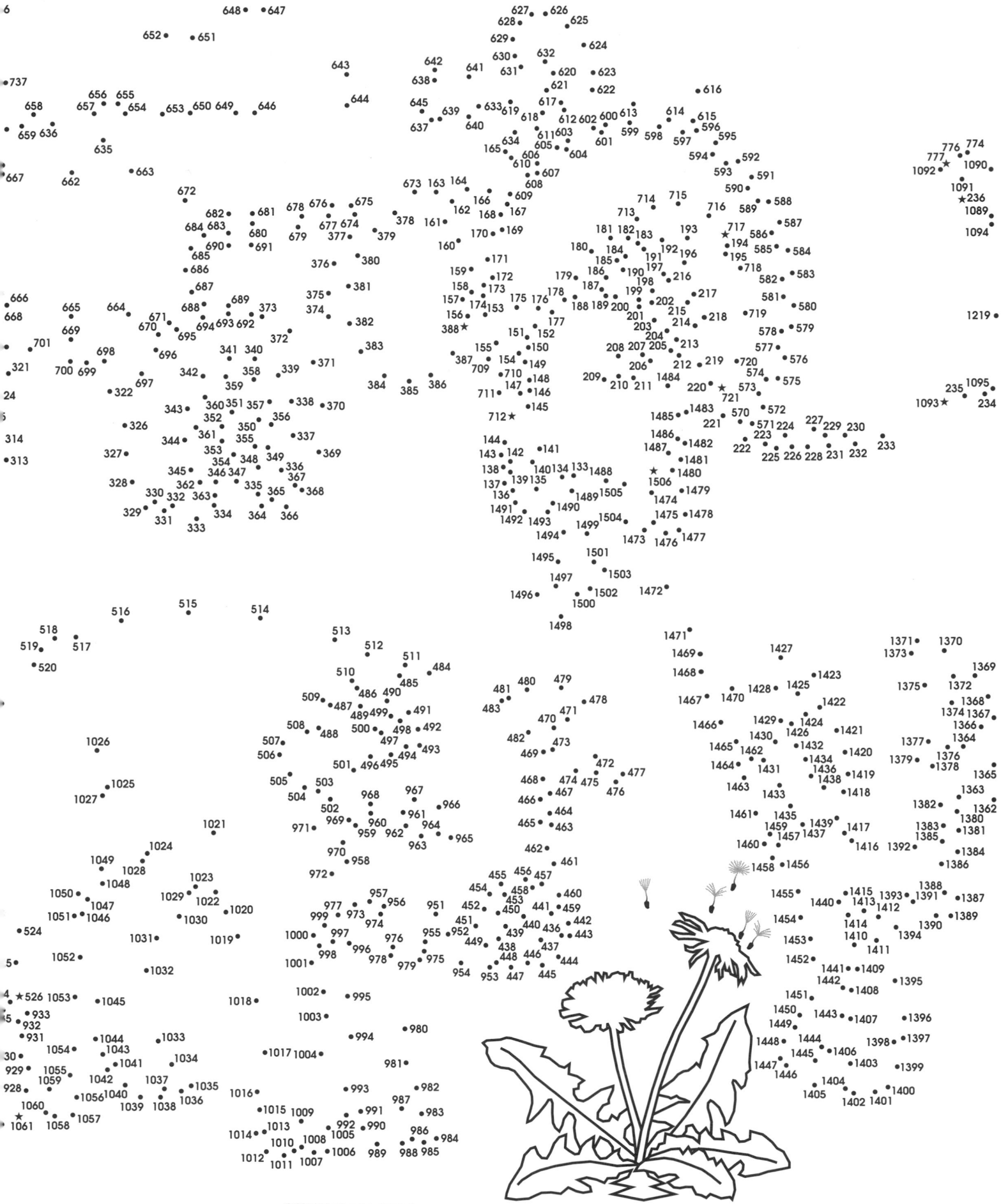

© 2014 Monkeying Around

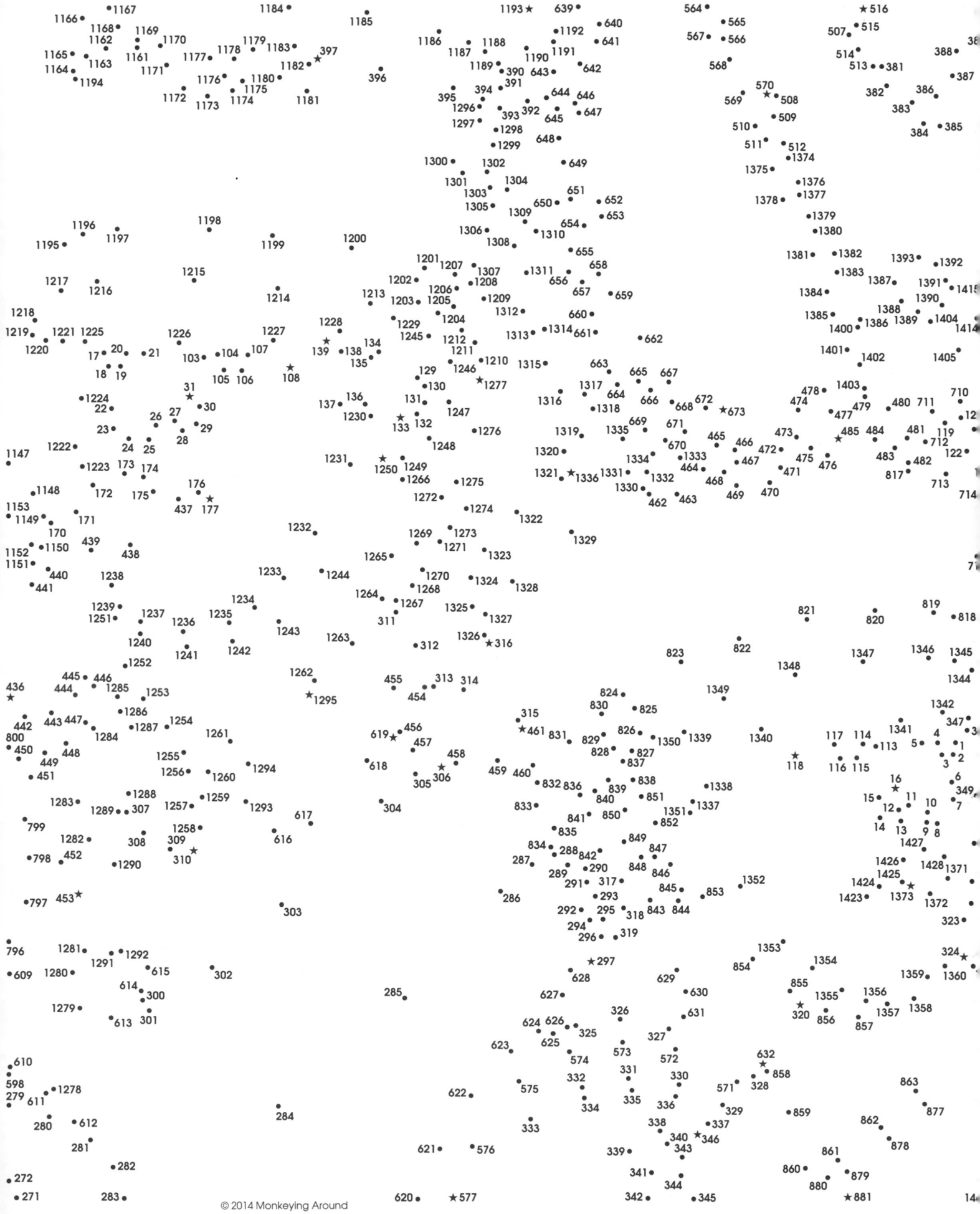

© 2014 Monkeying Around

3 Pages

Stop at each star (★), then skip to the next number and start your line again.

End ★ 1239

* **Tip:** Long lines, use a ruler.

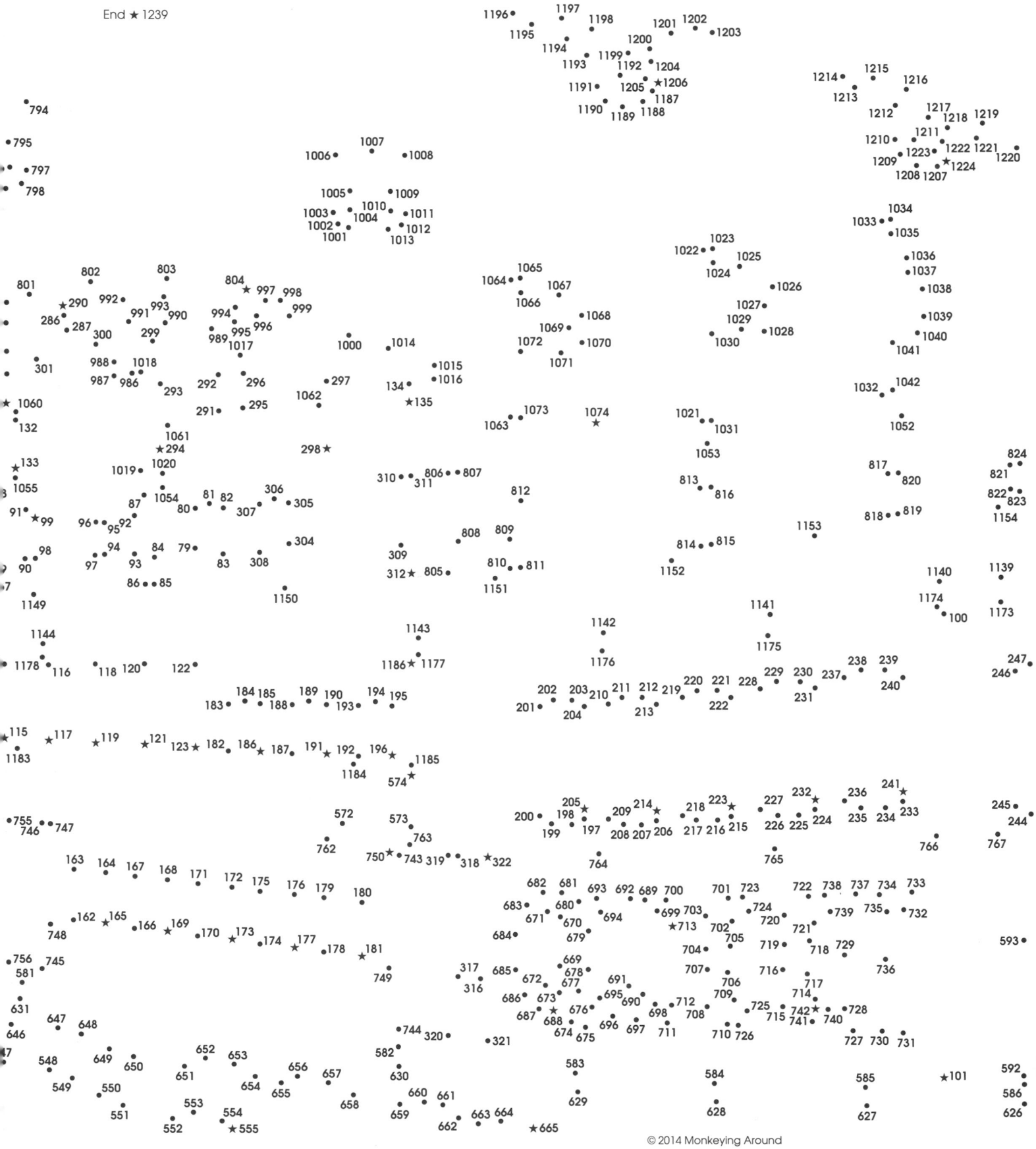

© 2014 Monkeying Around

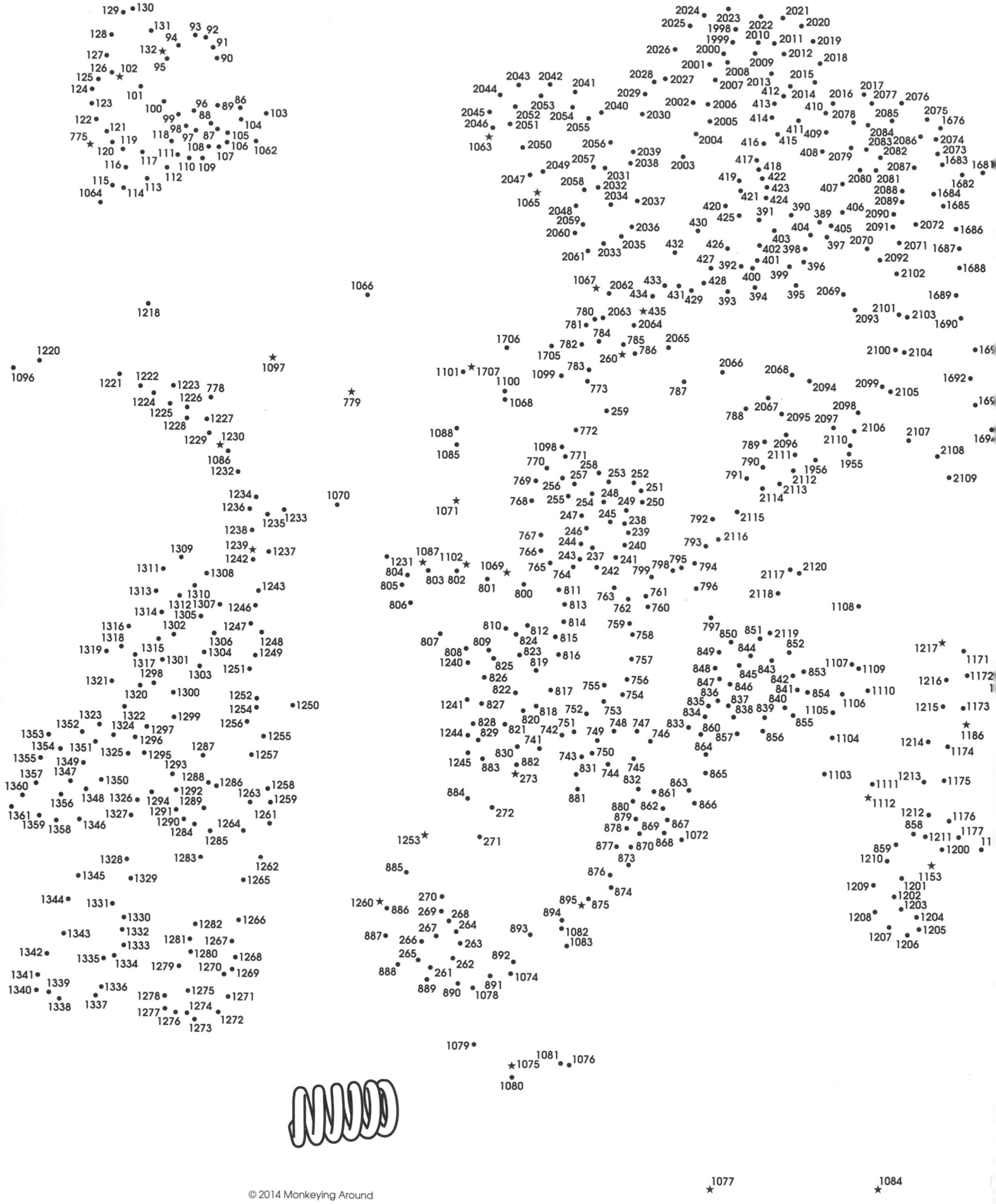

© 2014 Monkeying Around

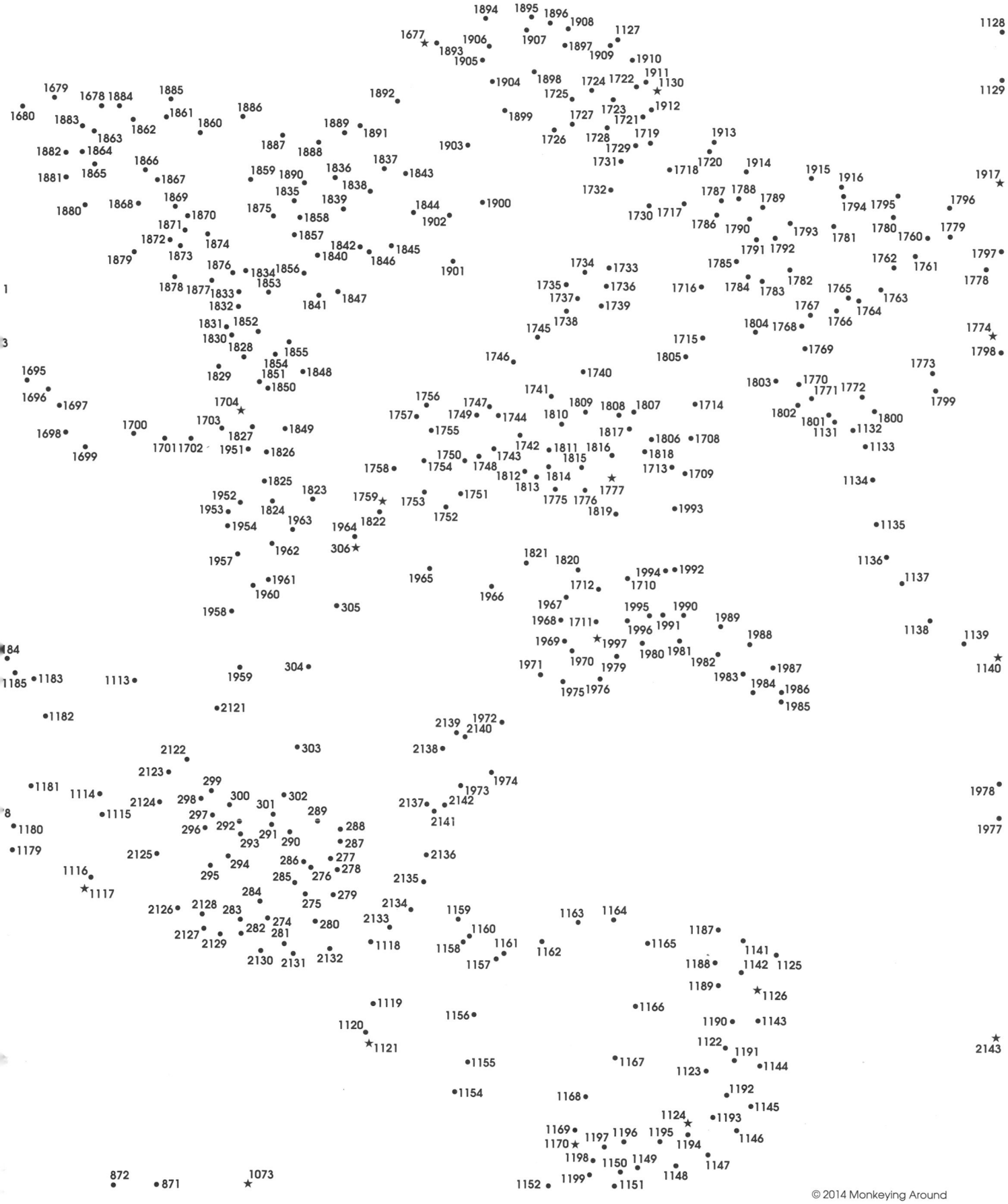

© 2014 Monkeying Around

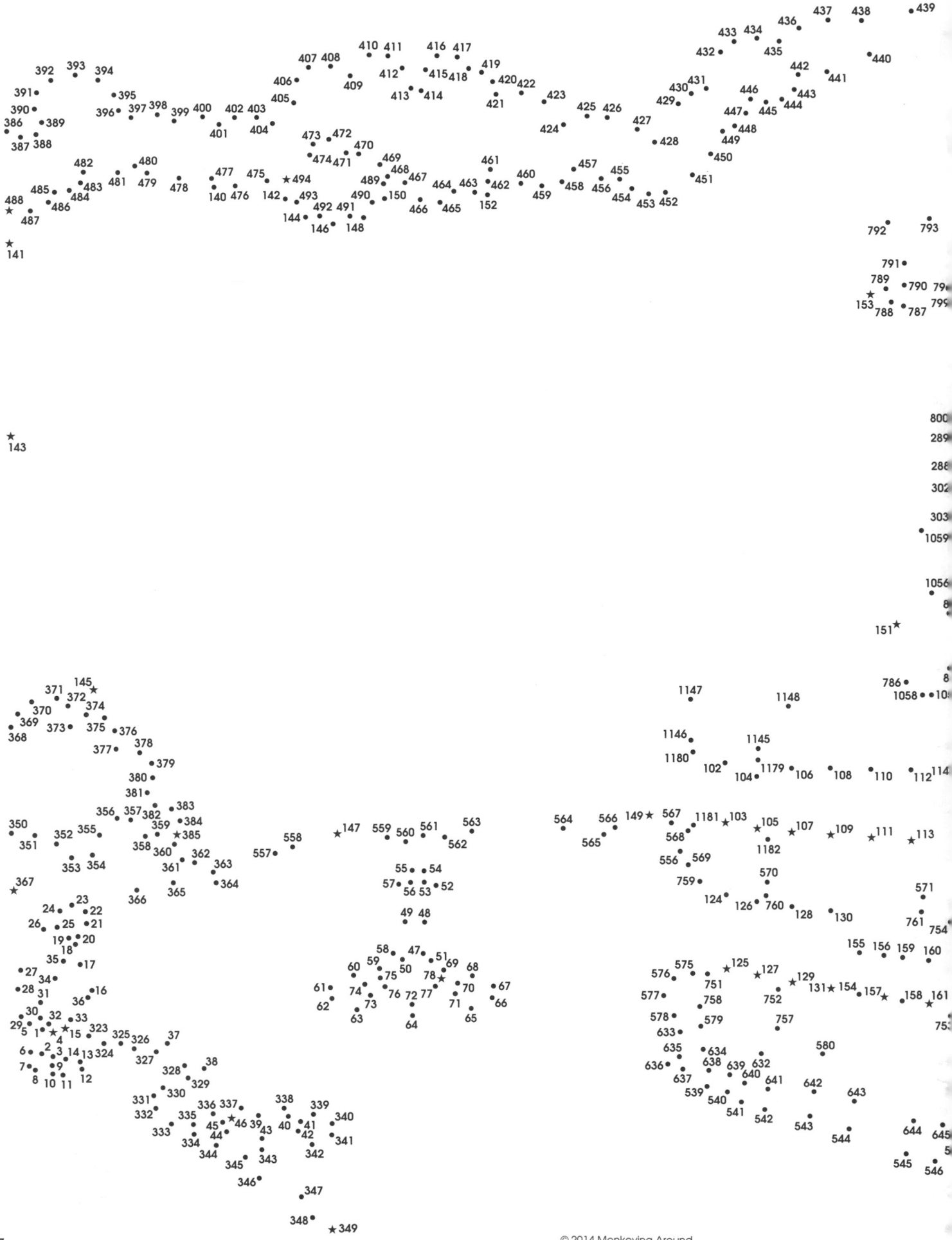

© 2014 Monkeying Around

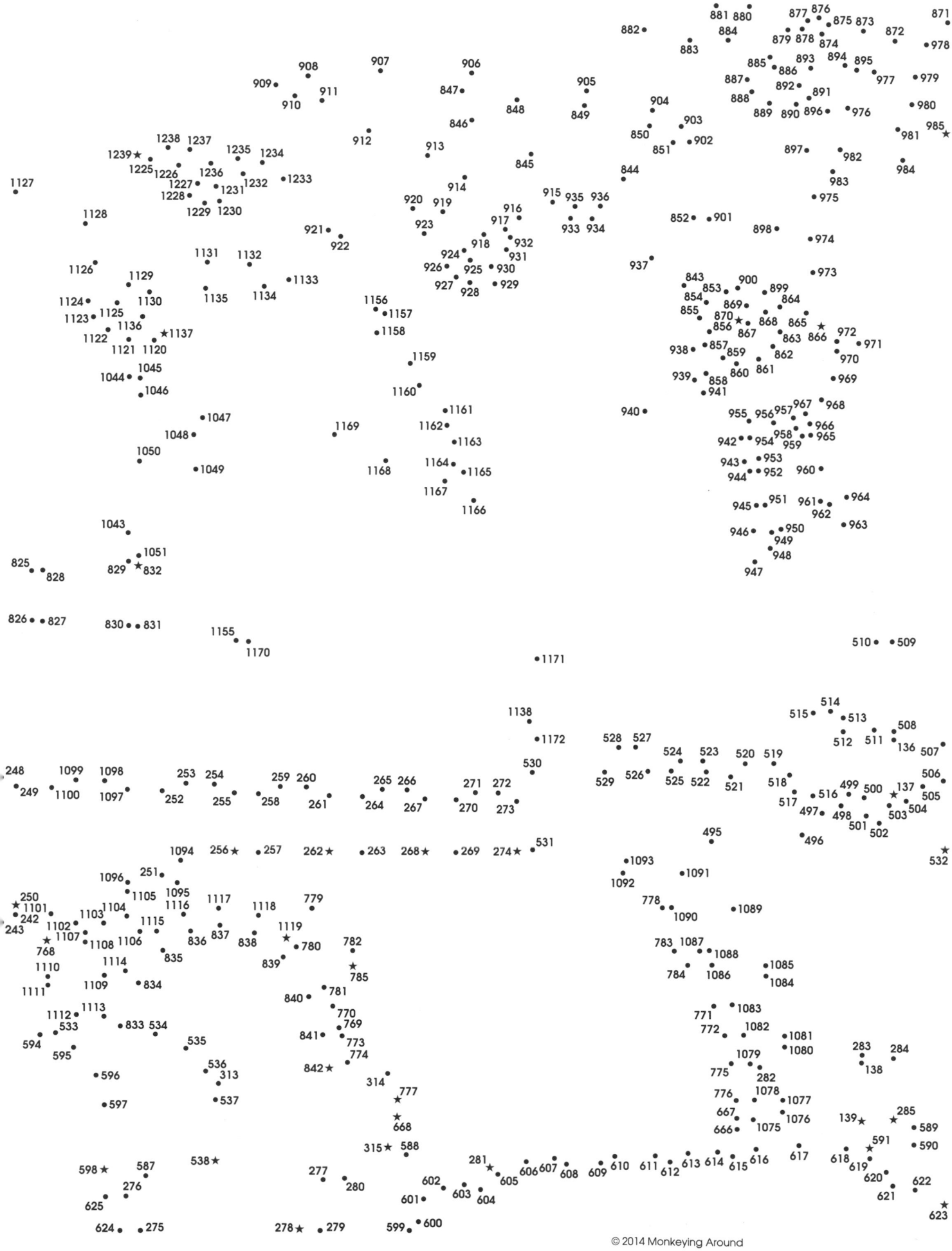

© 2014 Monkeying Around

Alpha Dots

Start with the word "ace", and connect all the words in alphabetical order, ending with the word "zoo".

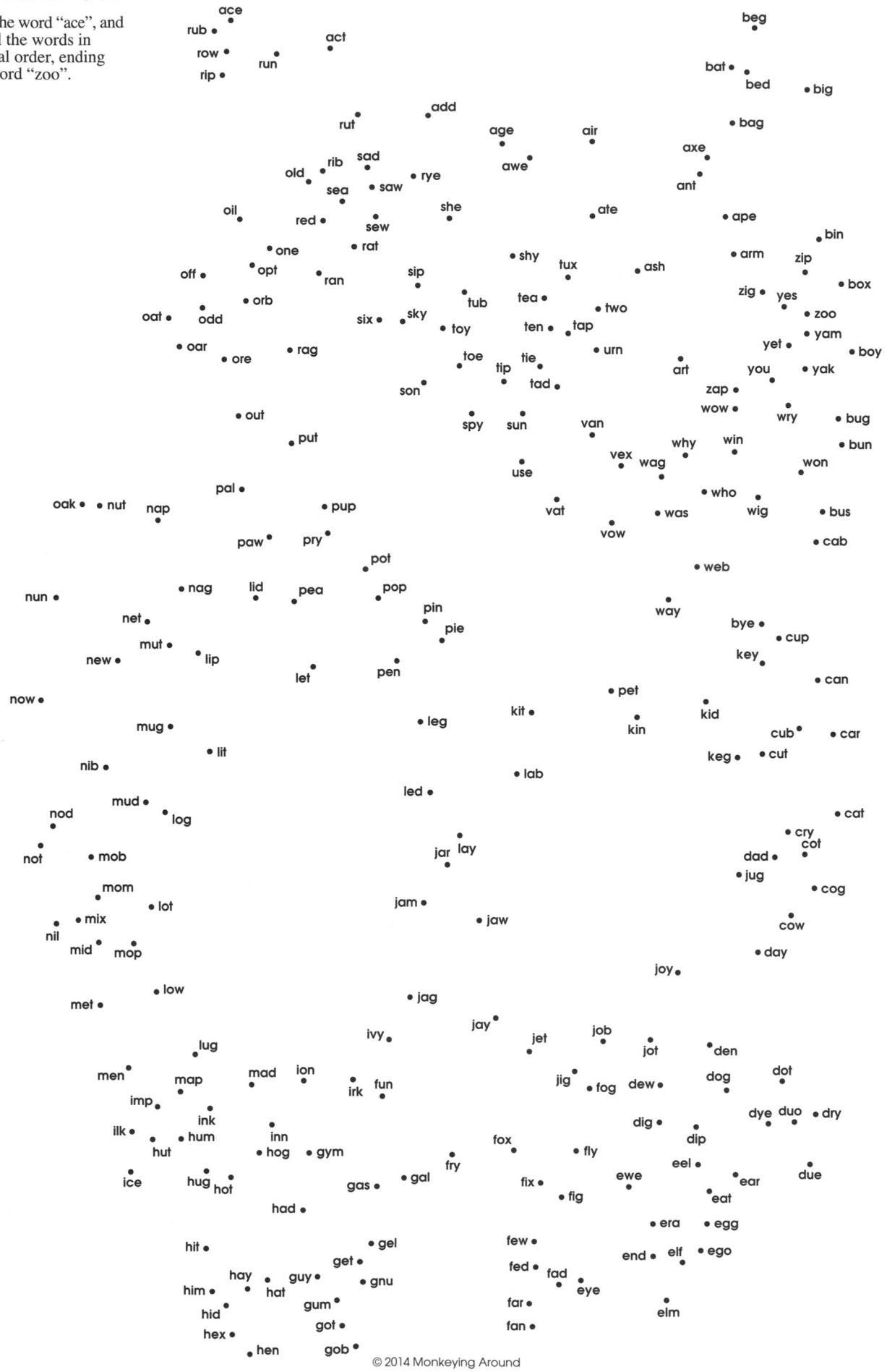

© 2014 Monkeying Around

* **Tip:** Aim for the middle of each number.

Numbers

Start at the circled number 001. Connect numbers in sequential order, passing through extra numbers. End at circled 210.

761	464	356	564	266	662	862	388	533	893	368	699	912	716	406	426	609	523	416	457	668	833	937	712						
811	903	908	684	561	468	879	200	650	201	584	596	449	351	685	992	807	510	638	506	496	734	602	384						
633	514	445	276	420	600	688	566	424	665	990	202	372	599	378	813	645	996	816	798	568	453	746	442						
465	546	428	924	827	264	199	277	987	489	952	608	972	853	723	647	919	882	949	284	858	382	406	905						
968	851	622	390	758	854	755	438	846	950	534	802	502	528	837	593	406	652	417	435	586	376	697	404						
482	778	545	353	477	794	927	840	206	804	205	654	874	773	964	826	740	904	413	572	895	431	291	808						
419	676	803	547	574	014	526	412	207	721	959	204	425	203	559	782	430	849	521	705	535	916	804	605	693	802	549	891	644	978
616	405	784	015	905	614	595	013	601	869	728	210	399	582	790	625	466	005	776	956	482	274	501	515	701	422	909	703	379	747
809	731	984	427	768	994	686	867	012	208	209	009	571	008	497	006	884	186	004	787	361	657	232	800	508	744	507	400	863	730
646	926	745	777	366	649	198	763	856	611	780	768	931	841	007	187	866	185	003	433	642	263	513	914	403	886	365	576	910	488
562	423	016	812	515	715	831	630	552	011	010	427	984	776	188	184	001	002	733	605	759	885	726	907	708	509	448	999	896	631
754	460	906	493	971	197	796	853	498	191	469	192	189	588	675	785	366	474	935	985	358	218	842	974	233	682	792	474	658	923
696	017	724	835	555	485	583	475	986	663	426	918	700	855	575	715	183	639	666	579	815	423	965	445	381	386	459	570	890	671
364	844	947	196	883	445	453	703	190	667	573	797	917	604	727	179	752	932	177	789	176	730	222	615	379	878	626	902	766	478
664	018	719	874	195	706	631	501	193	473	126	948	872	180	538	750	178	876	653	751	174	175	629	893	231	966	541	437	581	771
491	118	619	749	580	948	194	872	125	411	260	127	262	128	181	182	377	265	172	173	268	899	518	637	532	701	212	829	993	591
553	364	119	908	120	371	939	124	523	257	447	503	242	241	902	910	635	463	171	872	818	267	976	587	393	825	904	439	732	527
998	836	455	019	404	967	748	123	254	255	560	883	920	239	055	129	467	234	925	636	473	547	508	946	805	669	756	632	957	410
117	531	900	592	951	121	122	512	325	252	249	243	240	056	401	237	235	278	167	520	935	775	165	857	471	690	472	272	563	285
937	962	921	469	290	588	023	022	251	250	408	247	484	057	238	130	788	329	273	462	170	576	819	824	164	929	779	446	413	551
116	714	656	375	787	672	583	024	820	960	911	021	765	244	245	770	641	961	451	166	271	981	494	270	915	163	901	797	767	259
795	367	940	608	906	597	628	769	680	760	345	839	246	229	230	928	516	490	650	282	930	456	145	383	409	394	875	533	969	357
360	115	507	673	458	860	774	888	025	020	470	610	228	227	709	504	799	369	168	762	283	144	619	678	146	548	783	946	694	852
660	913	114	497	261	529	356	602	781	058	651	934	220	221	867	226	408	750	835	169	287	374	743	398	421	868	603	954	355	543
963	838	495	859	113	112	558	387	786	791	936	537	627	965	567	380	656	397	280	723	407	143	418	793	139	147	958	162	655	360
880	540	870	970	850	846	500	901	713	059	629	798	099	213	834	951	452	611	429	661	593	659	933	140	681	138	524	772	440	810
735	814	483	668	441	111	698	060	026	517	864	100	538	098	627	097	668	585	922	132	683	288	945	432	707	613	687	909	161	577
742	557	873	565	717	979	584	711	938	027	544	368	657	729	861	621	481	131	606	481	520	443	142	141	733	385	592	832	643	719
898	590	110	824	408	061	763	803	546	975	718	101	618	207	211	596	809	223	359	490	153	876	435	977	617	528	137	789	394	822
724	536	109	702	350	696	468	395	995	542	482	973	351	279	997	096	710	054	741	989	286	429	133	692	134	800	386	148	700	281
108	568	881	905	866	443	613	675	706	738	813	433	626	878	275	210	214	217	216	691	894	326	152	991	548	135	136	883	806	160
597	370	822	742	942	692	988	833	103	577	102	380	621	897	095	208	530	215	053	595	712	289	705	363	759	526	668	358	939	420
950	536	745	493	971	383	953	707	643	941	525	029	087	088	375	716	209	785	753	485	623	292	154	635	415	605	985	149	734	628
107	370	431	932	353	624	104	062	554	028	428	520	030	089	094	093	953	051	052	428	736	293	523	830	151	784	575	815	472	159
253	106	762	534	105	035	034	983	754	980	086	514	902	989	739	883	763	050	687	922	735	571	691	607	574	696	150	480	948	651
664	409	248	507	502	720	814	546	499	635	402	031	952	504	092	944	458	756	352	598	612	943	294	481	155	423	751	730	158	538
491	979	528	749	927	423	631	415	817	085	567	090	091	354	822	867	206	986	432	442	402	506	496	384	602	522	156	157	541	973
550	465	036	623	404	064	740	063	033	032	046	380	367	397	049	403	380	873	408	459	602	295	391	422	746	400	579	818	510	976
514	836	757	625	065	813	942	084	408	533	753	743	048	923	532	624	902	825	989	381	296	707	473	373	980	640	636	436	736	508
709	684	517	625	524	529	424	663	074	960	806	047	885	585	960	982	627	413	593	894	432	912	586	382	674	476	562	725	529	462
590	501	921	739	903	082	083	864	704	696	768	550	445	978	729	613	621	764	654	567	419	965	635	667	480	737	668	477	375	951
441	037	967	066	081	852	075	528	724	371	363	045	672	875	988	709	549	874	633	743	456	606	457	916	482	877	894	732	501	818
795	539	940	838	600	821	639	076	917	073	411	953	416	935	564	946	378	487	793	934	587	956	523	454	845	455	466	925	636	391
498	038	395	067	650	761	621	666	947	417	721	586	972	882	356	675	911	768	892	681	646	851	433	653	738	887	963	362	586	725
660	913	790	497	080	499	572	667	658	072	678	884	529	949	864	961	876	943	751	598	888	946	628	697	900	593	894	565	432	487
486	647	495	859	873	640	415	077	823	737	414	823	907	396	549	891	606	594	224	720	616	890	723	570	775	662	862	964	833	413
880	540	483	546	497	079	078	916	464	877	862	044	556	670	579	682	975	836	977	617	811	591	918	770	561	468	840	752	650	932
687	400	039	623	068	571	378	460	071	455	578	653	444	848	974	747	741	672	438	409	850	644	461	408	863	379	688	566	409	740
612	531	648	962	717	069	433	070	731	887	403	867	548	873	863	658	520	593	943	543	957	891	637	924	827	782	899	526	978	489
898	456	610	040	713	853	642	699	513	914	043	886	752	494	708	488	815	472	797	900	562	628	459	570	890	671	432	555	656	634
941	603	356	702	994	455	759	839	628	714	665	509	448	999	896	955	651	871	761	668	461	567	644	860	766	478	763	365	762	818
832	981	881	583	637	041	358	541	042	542	470	682	792	609	371	726	392	923	782	893	991	392	982	437	581	771	597	611	504	733

© 2014 Monkeying Around

Stars

Stop at each star (★), then skip to the next number and start your line again.

End ★ 456

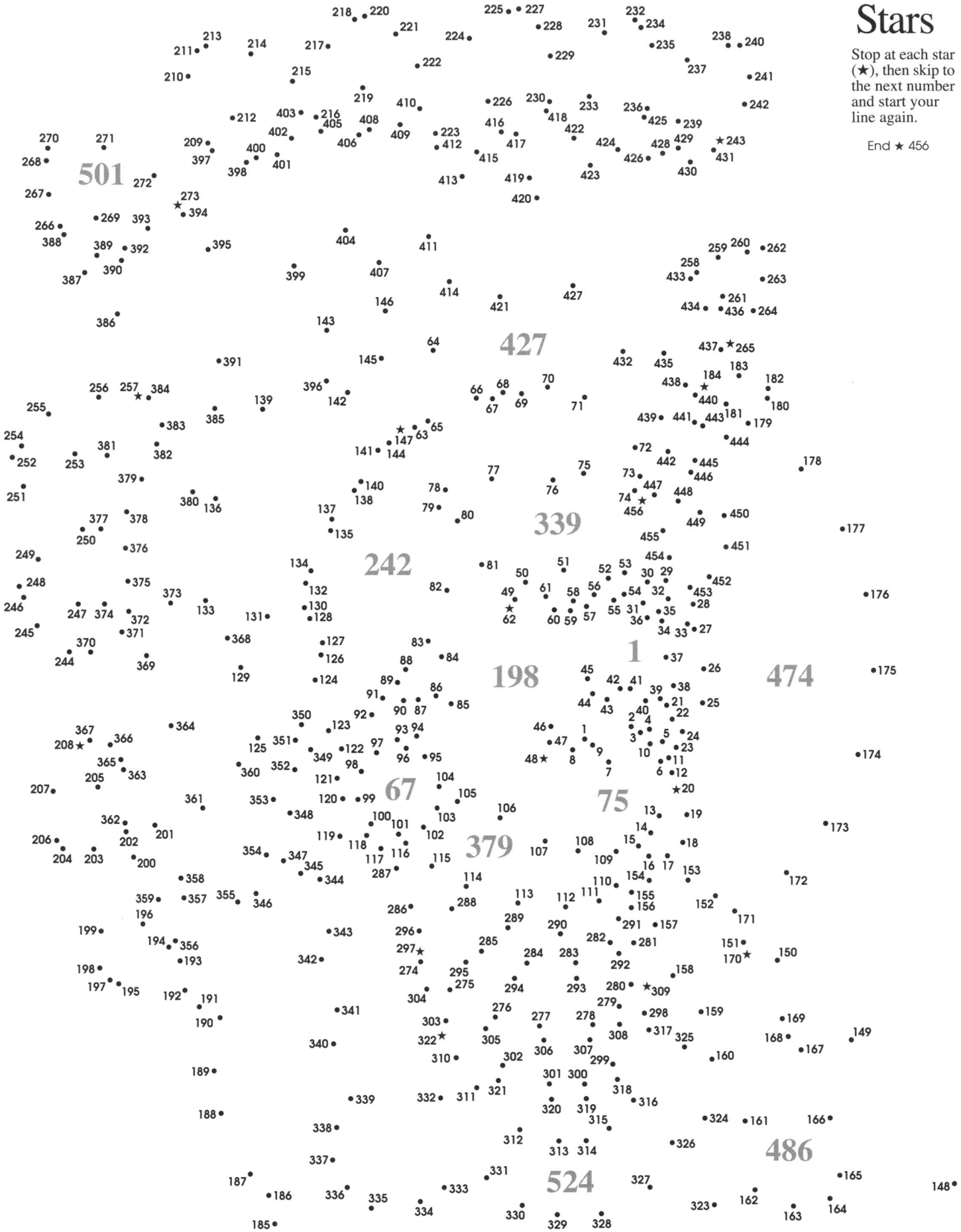

* Use the number clues in this puzzle to solve the puzzle on **page 33.**

© 2014 Monkeying Around

Stars

Stop at each star (★), then skip to the next number and start your line again.

End ★ 540

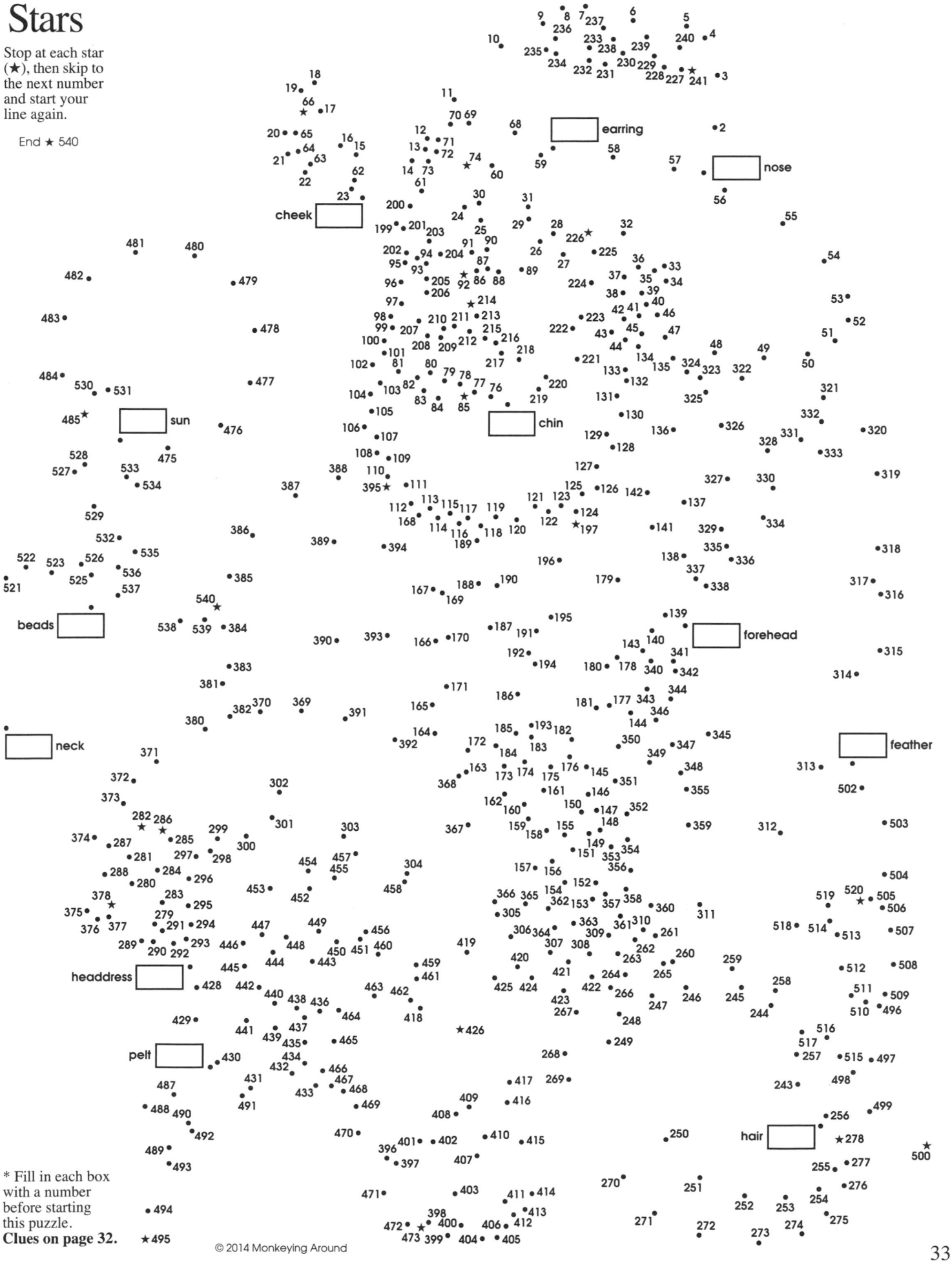

* Fill in each box with a number before starting this puzzle.
Clues on page 32.

© 2014 Monkeying Around

* **Tip:** Long lines, use a ruler.

Stars

Stop at each star (★), then skip to the next number and start your line again.

End ★ 718

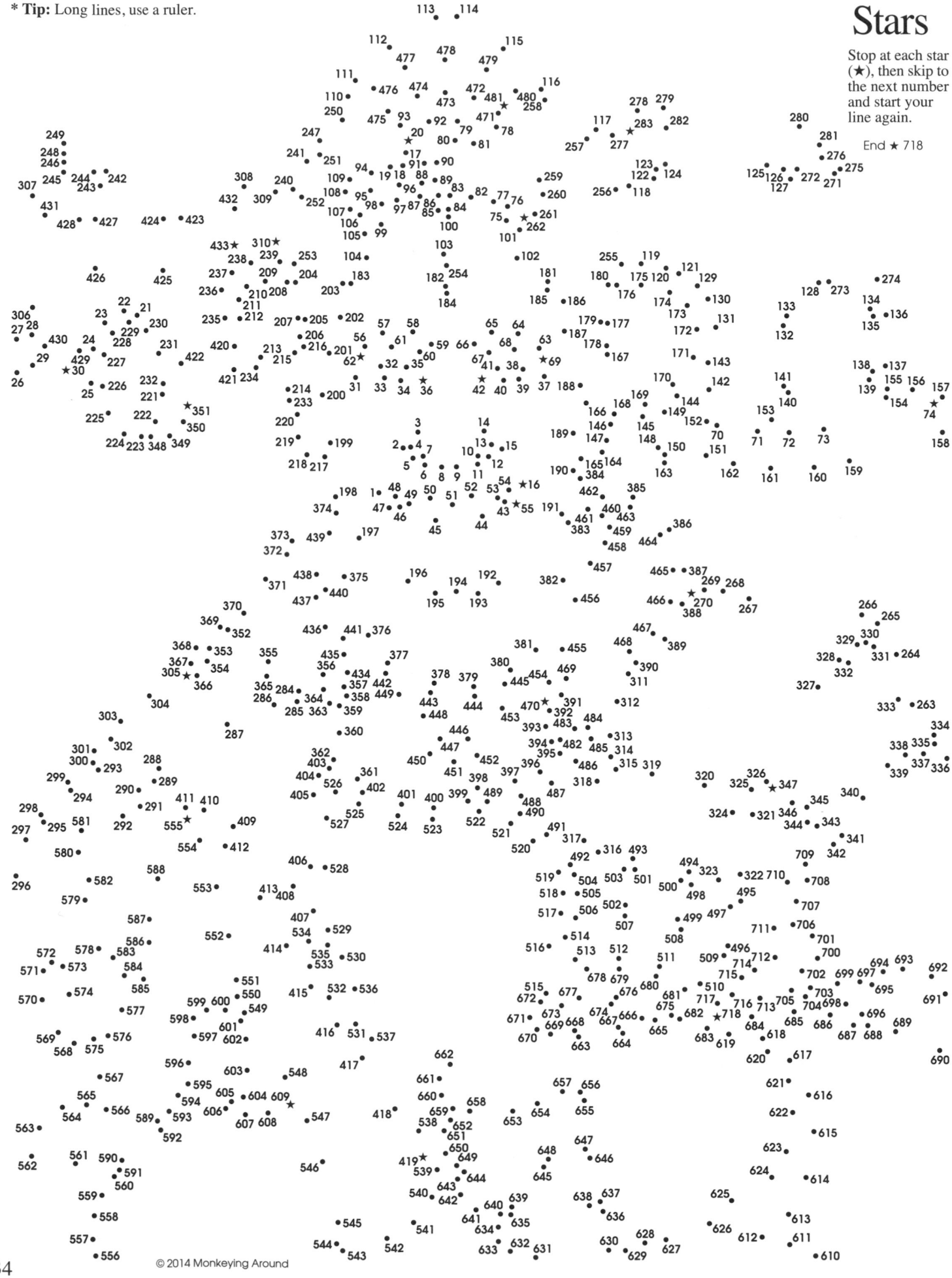

© 2014 Monkeying Around

No Dots!

Connect Numbers:

1 – 288
A – E

* **Tips:** Aim for the middle of each number.
Long lines, use a ruler.

© 2014 Monkeying Around

Scene

Stop at each bean sprout (𝍐), then skip to the next number and start your line again.

End 𝍐 548

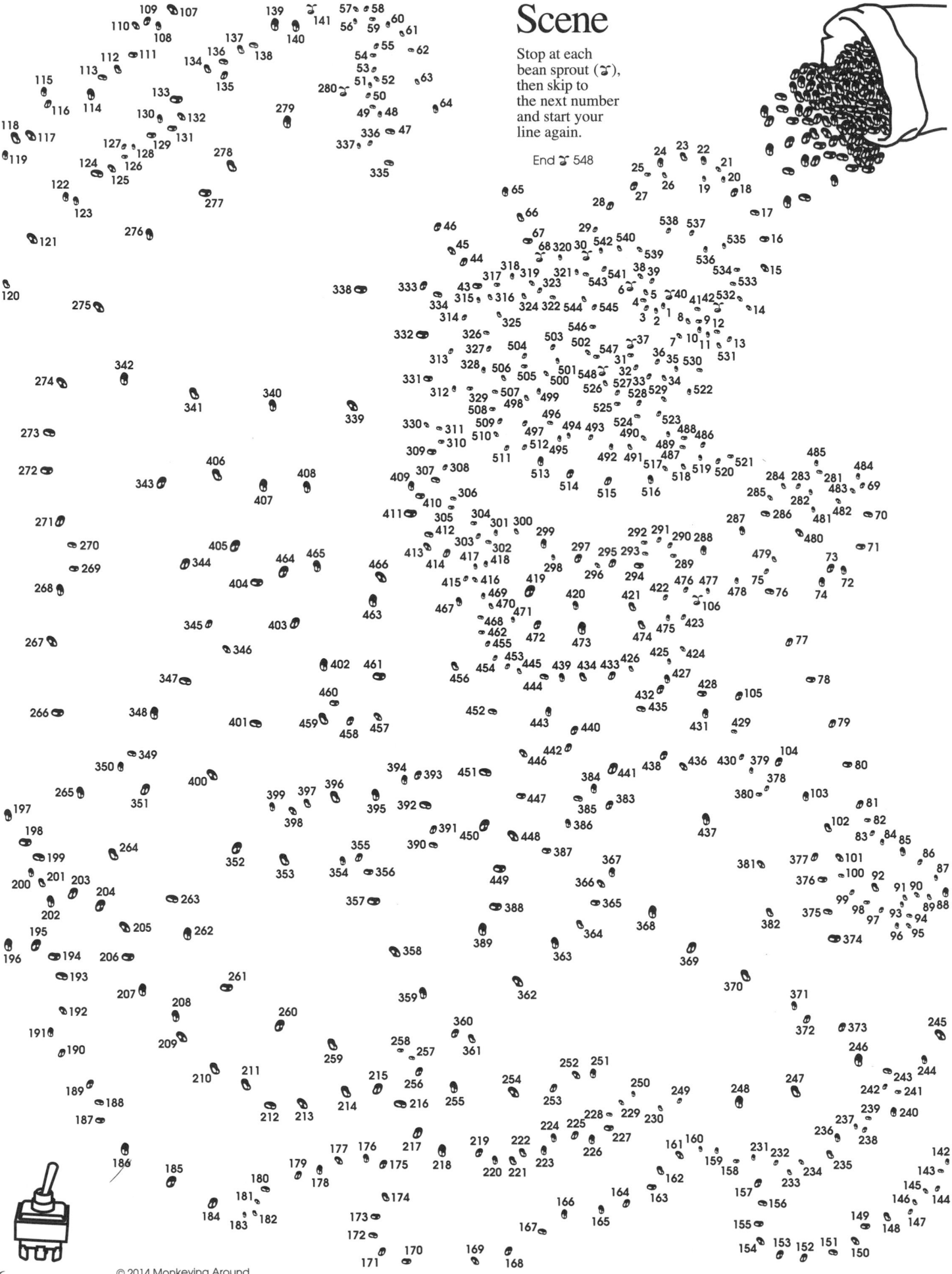

© 2014 Monkeying Around

ABC Sets

After connecting the "A" set, skip to the "B" set and start your line again. Repeat for "C" set, and so on.

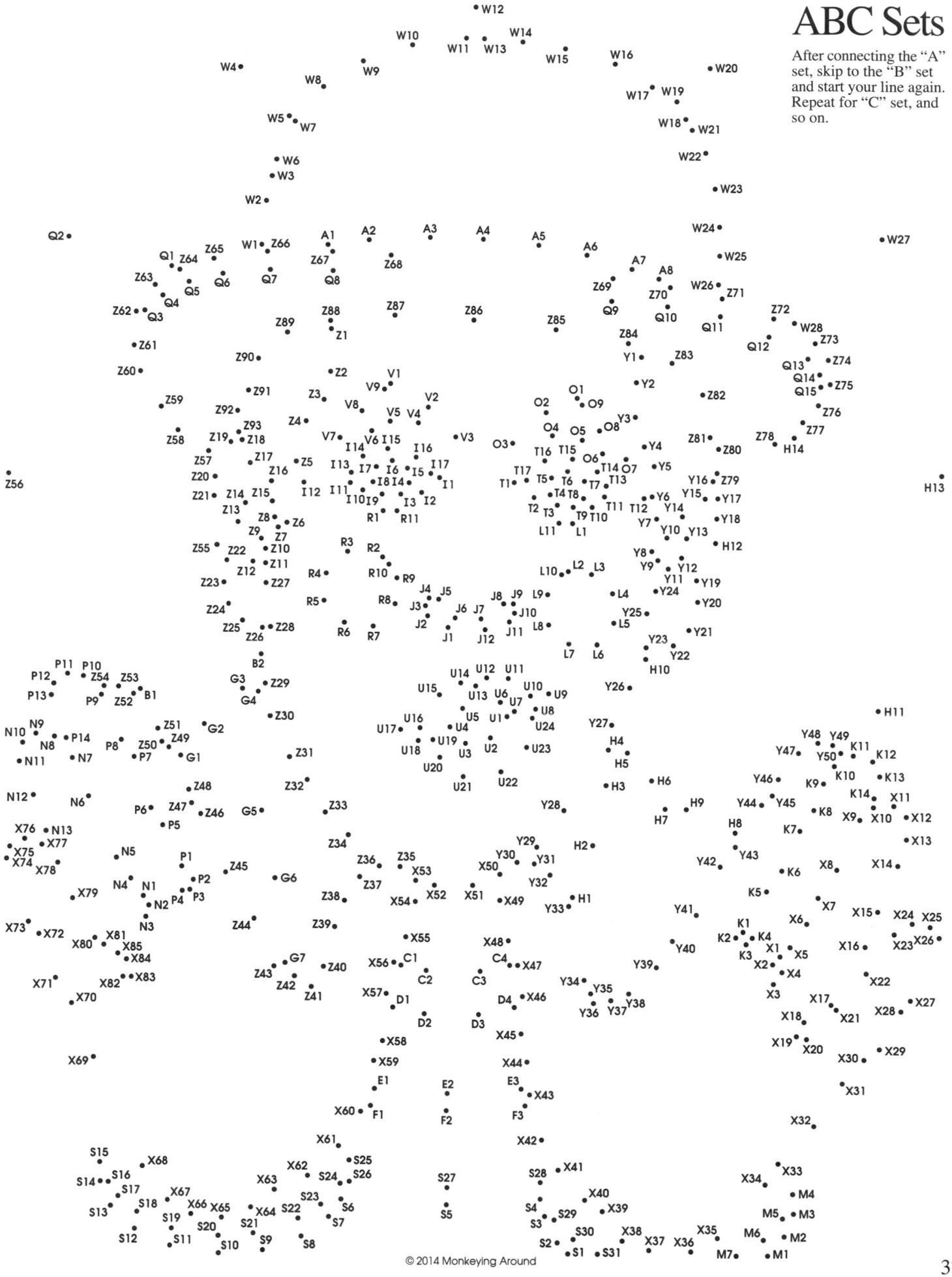

© 2014 Monkeying Around

Stars

Stop at each star (★), then skip to the next number and start your line again.

End ★ 241

* **Tip:** Long lines, use a ruler.

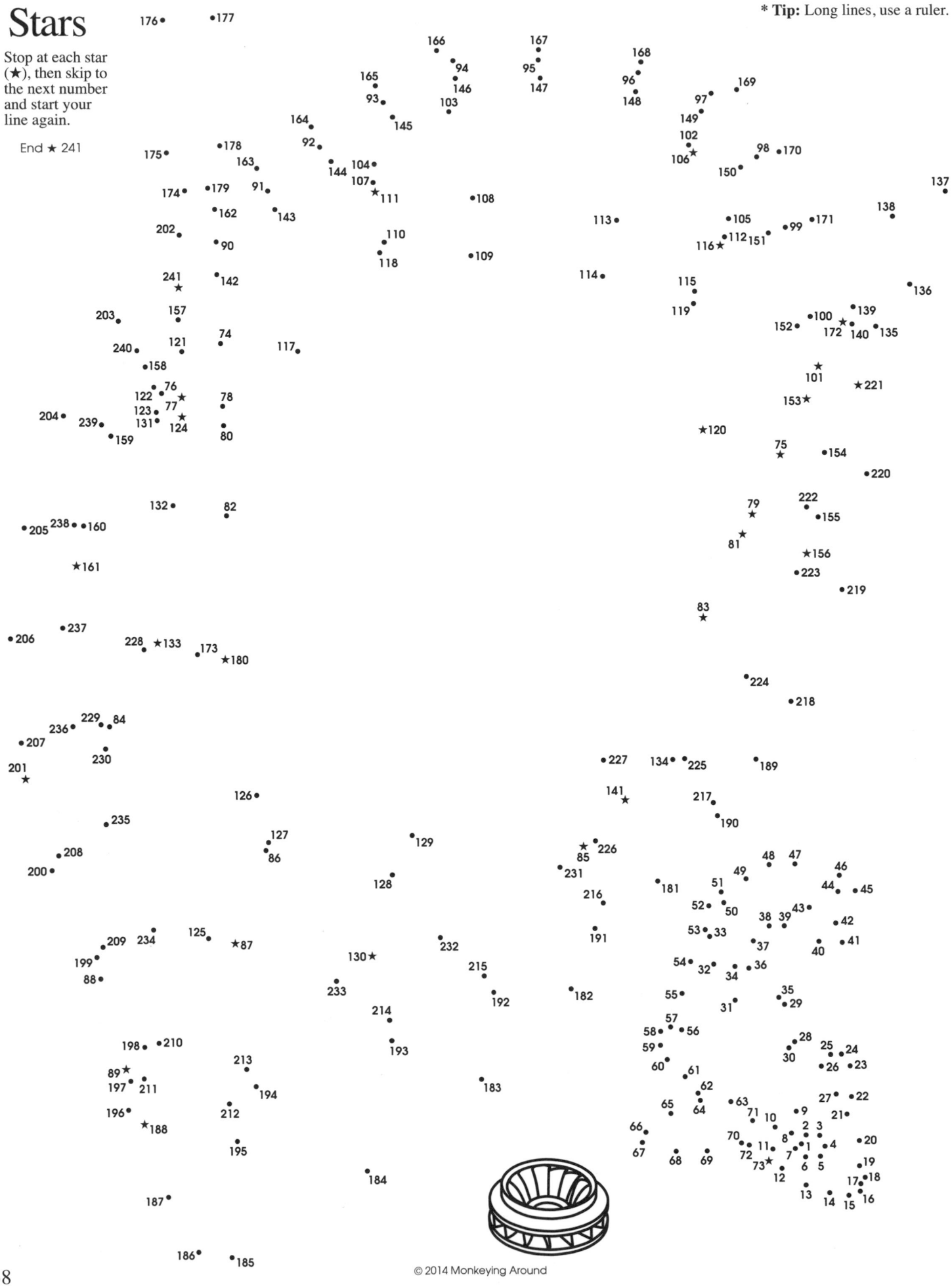

© 2014 Monkeying Around

Stars

Stop at each star (★), then skip to the next number and start your line again.

End ★ 625

* **Tip:** Long lines, use a ruler.

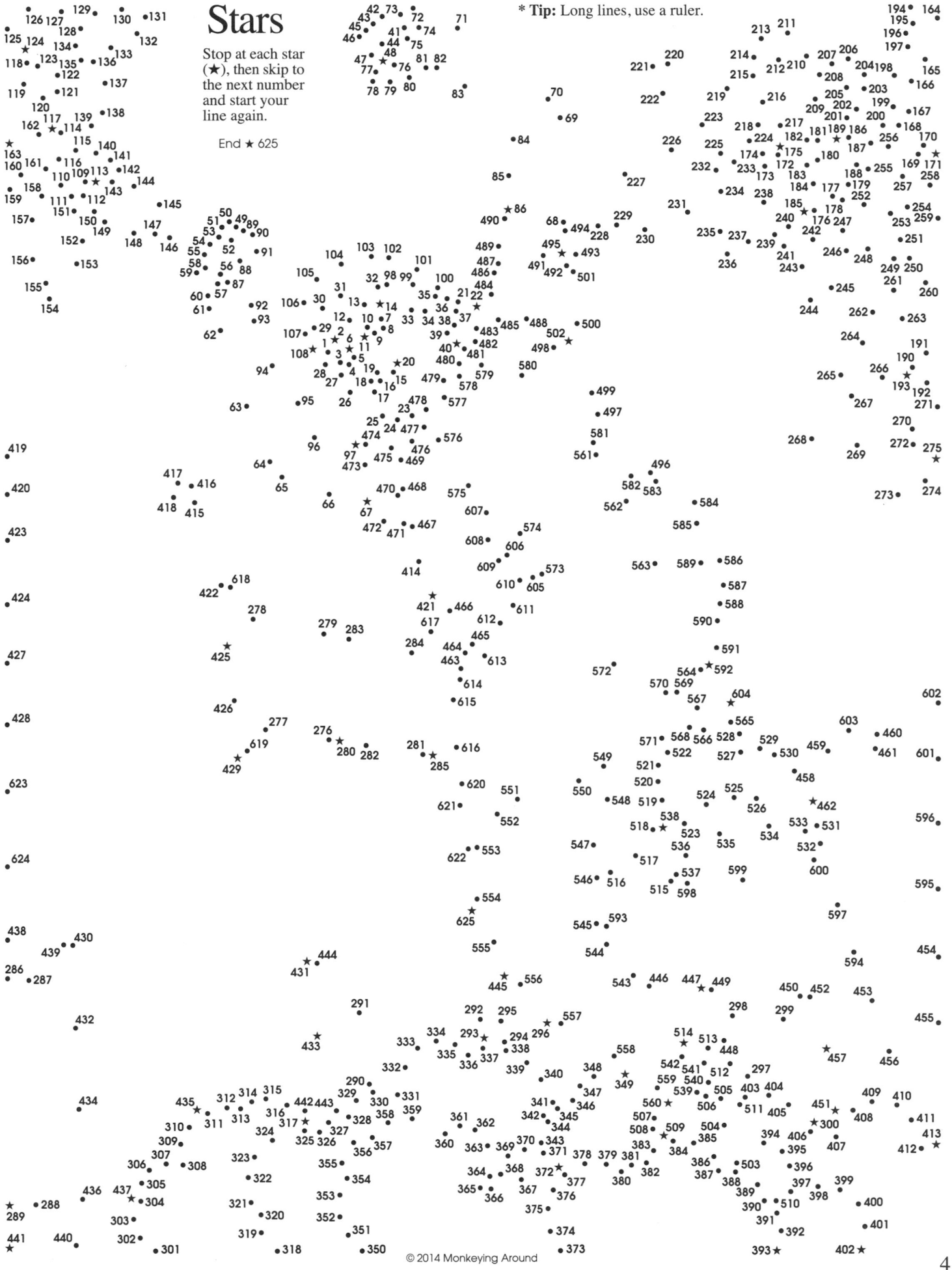

© 2014 Monkeying Around

Circuits

Complete each set of circuits using straight lines. Start at a circle and end at a circle to complete each circuit.

Complete circuit.

*** Tips:** Connect easy circuits until harder ones become clear. Long lines, use a ruler.

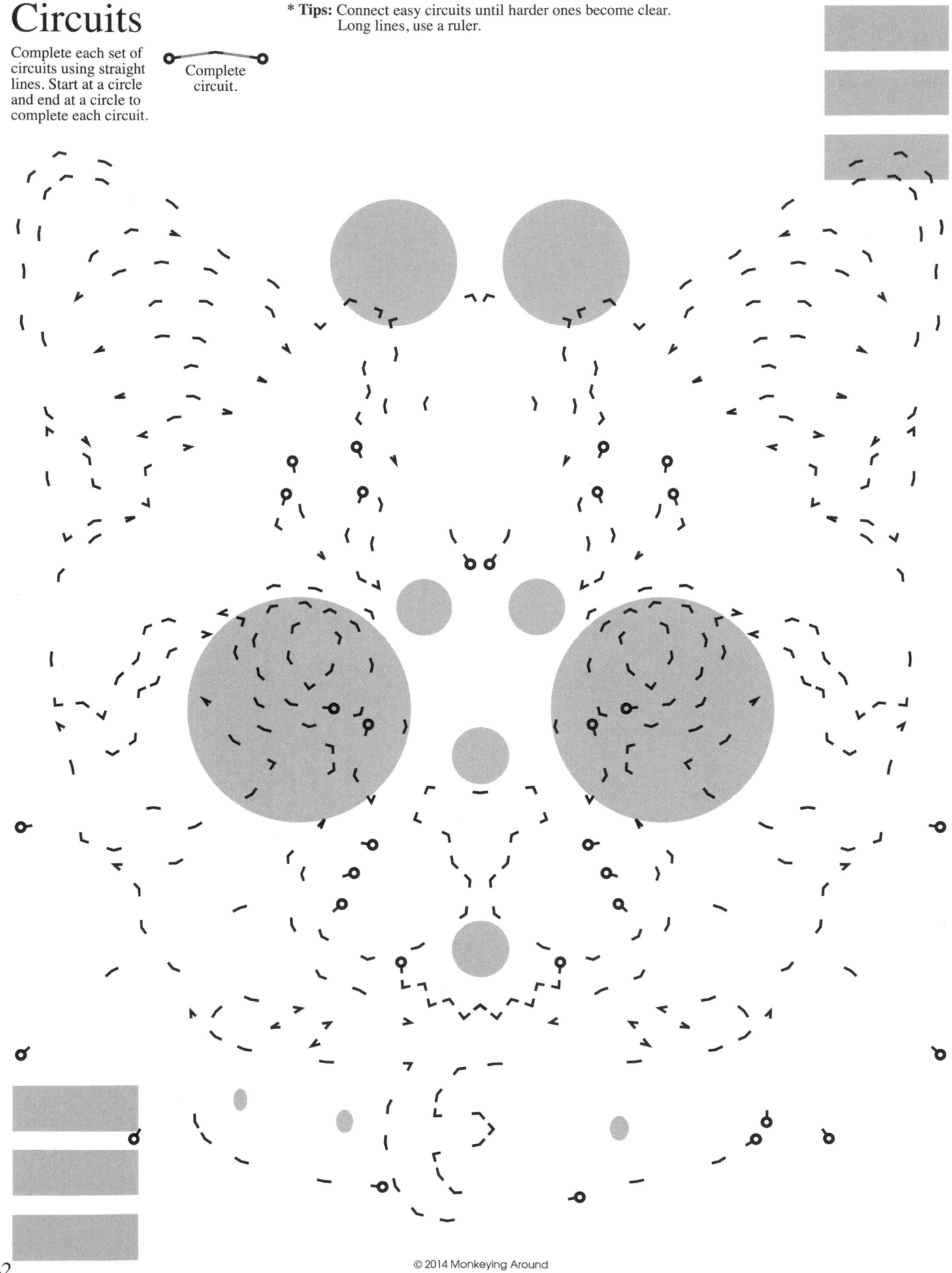

© 2014 Monkeying Around

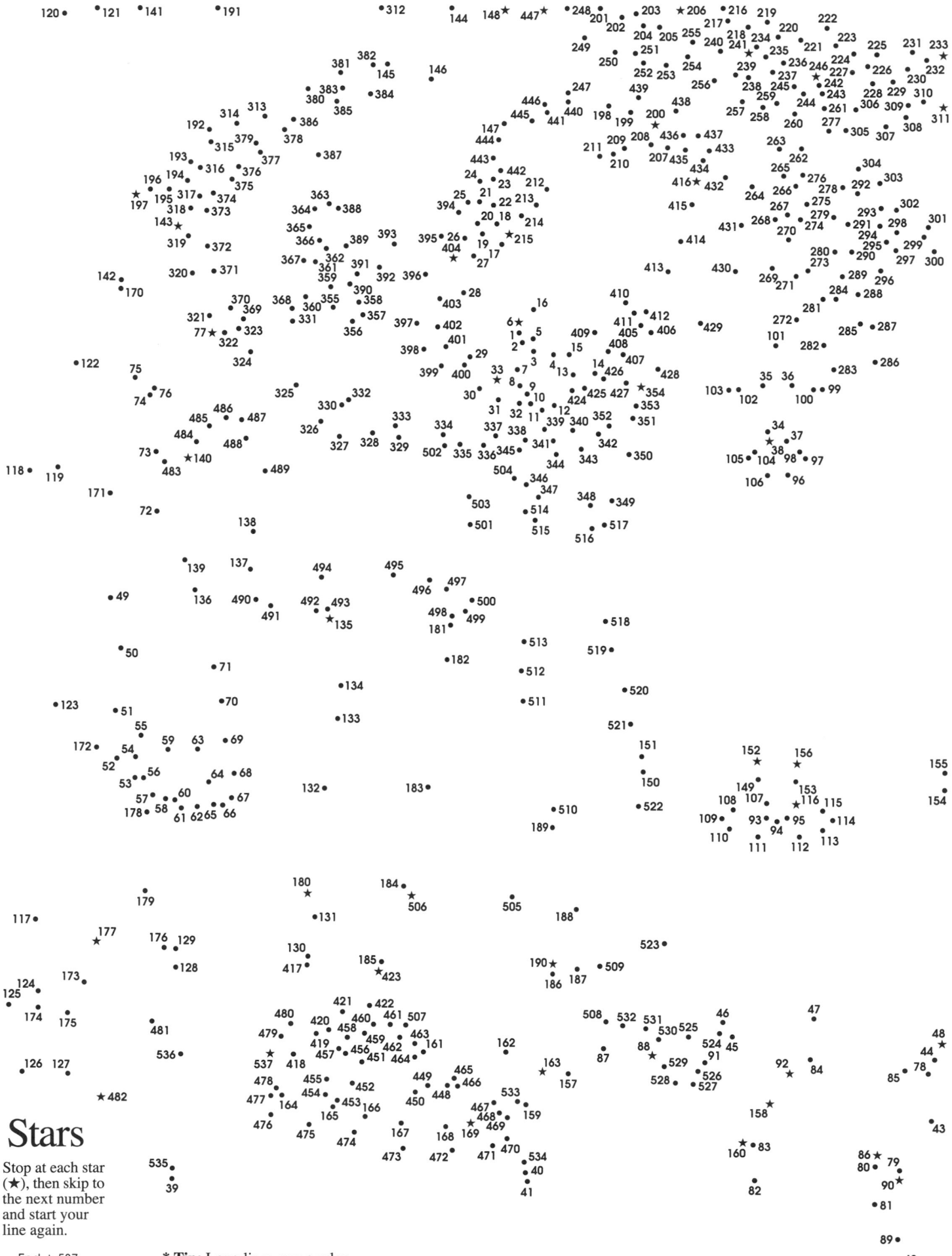

Stars

Stop at each star (★), then skip to the next number and start your line again.

End ★ 537

* **Tip:** Long lines, use a ruler.

© 2014 Monkeying Around

Sets

Stop your line after completing each set, then skip to the next set and start your line again.

- ❑ ● 1 thru 39
- ❑ ▲ 40 thru 60
- ❑ ■ 61 thru 115
- ❑ ♦ 116 thru 161
- ❑ ● 162 thru 180
- ❑ ▲ 181 thru 218
- ❑ ■ 219 thru 224
- ❑ ♦ 225 thru 258
- ❑ ● 259 thru 283
- ❑ ▲ 284 thru 293
- ❑ ■ 294 thru 358
- ❑ ♦ 359 thru 385
- ❑ ● 386 thru 431
- ❑ ▲ 432 thru 451
- ❑ ■ 452 thru 460
- ❑ ♦ 461 thru 500
- ❑ ● 501 thru 756

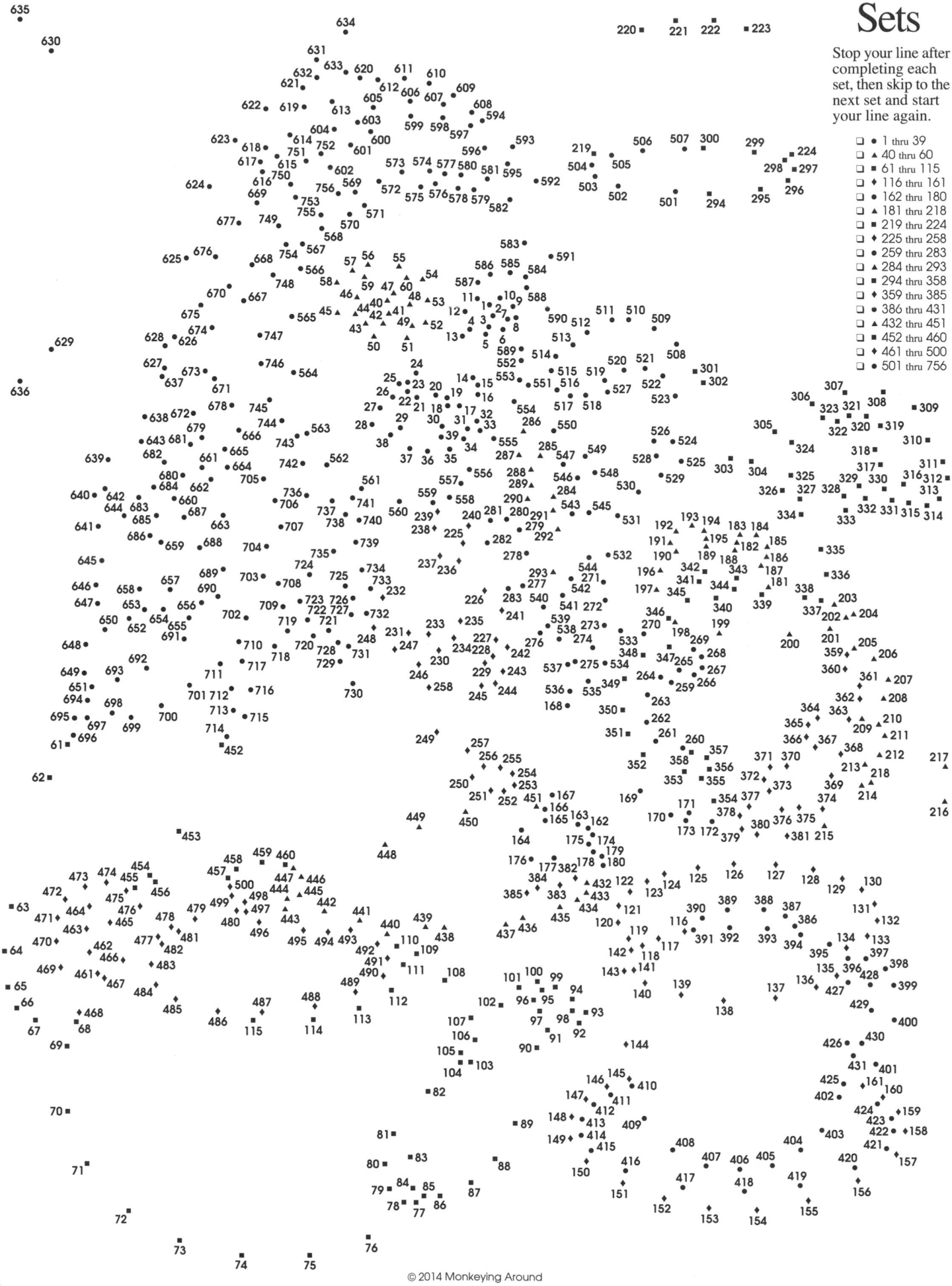

© 2014 Monkeying Around

Stars

Stop at each star (★), then skip to the next number and start your line again.

End ★368

1. Match each part to a word. (Clue on page where the part was found.)
2. Write corresponding number in empty lettered boxes.

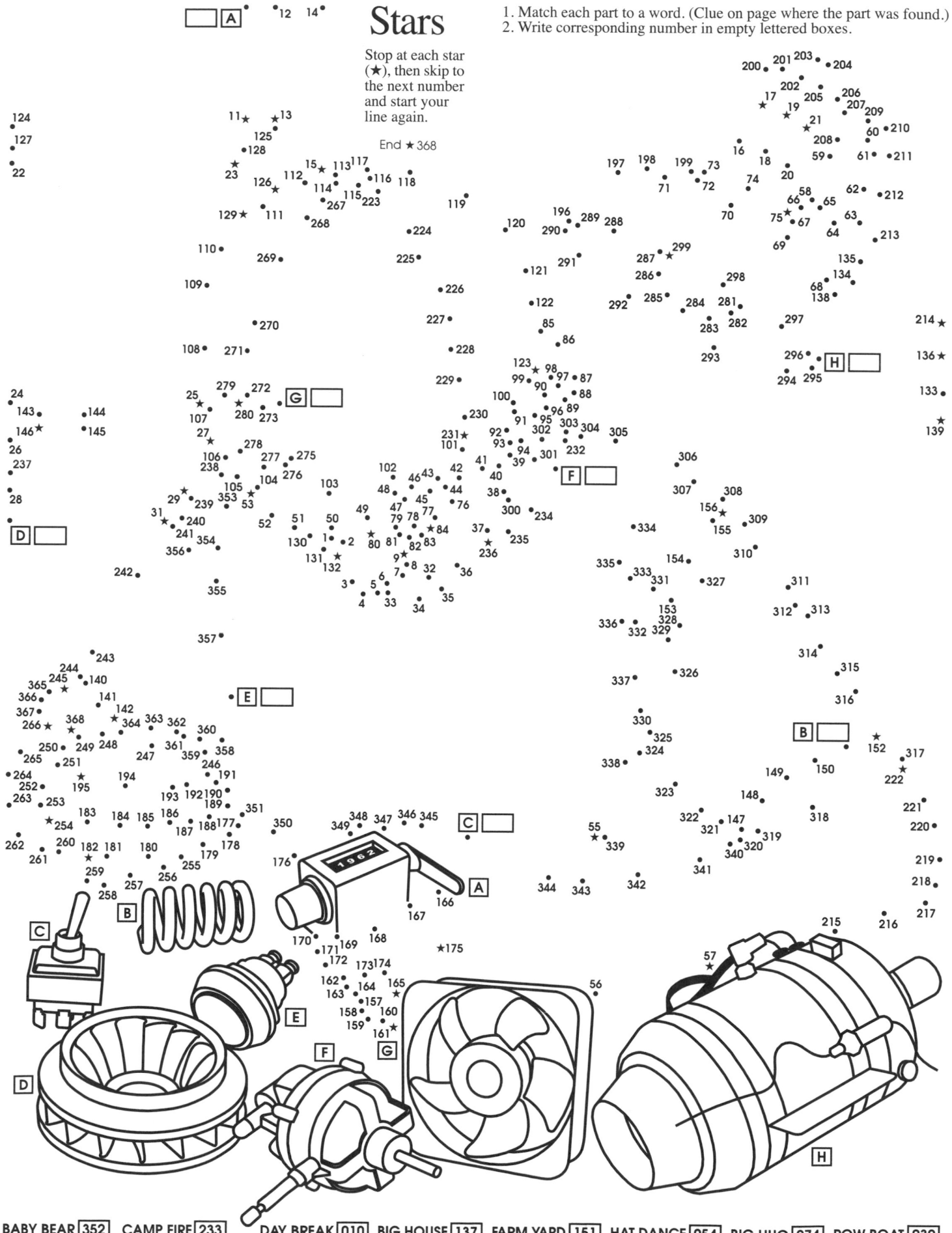

BABY BEAR [352] CAMP FIRE [233] DAY BREAK [010] BIG HOUSE [137] FARM YARD [151] HAT DANCE [054] BIG HUG [274] ROW BOAT [030]

© 2014 Monkeying Around

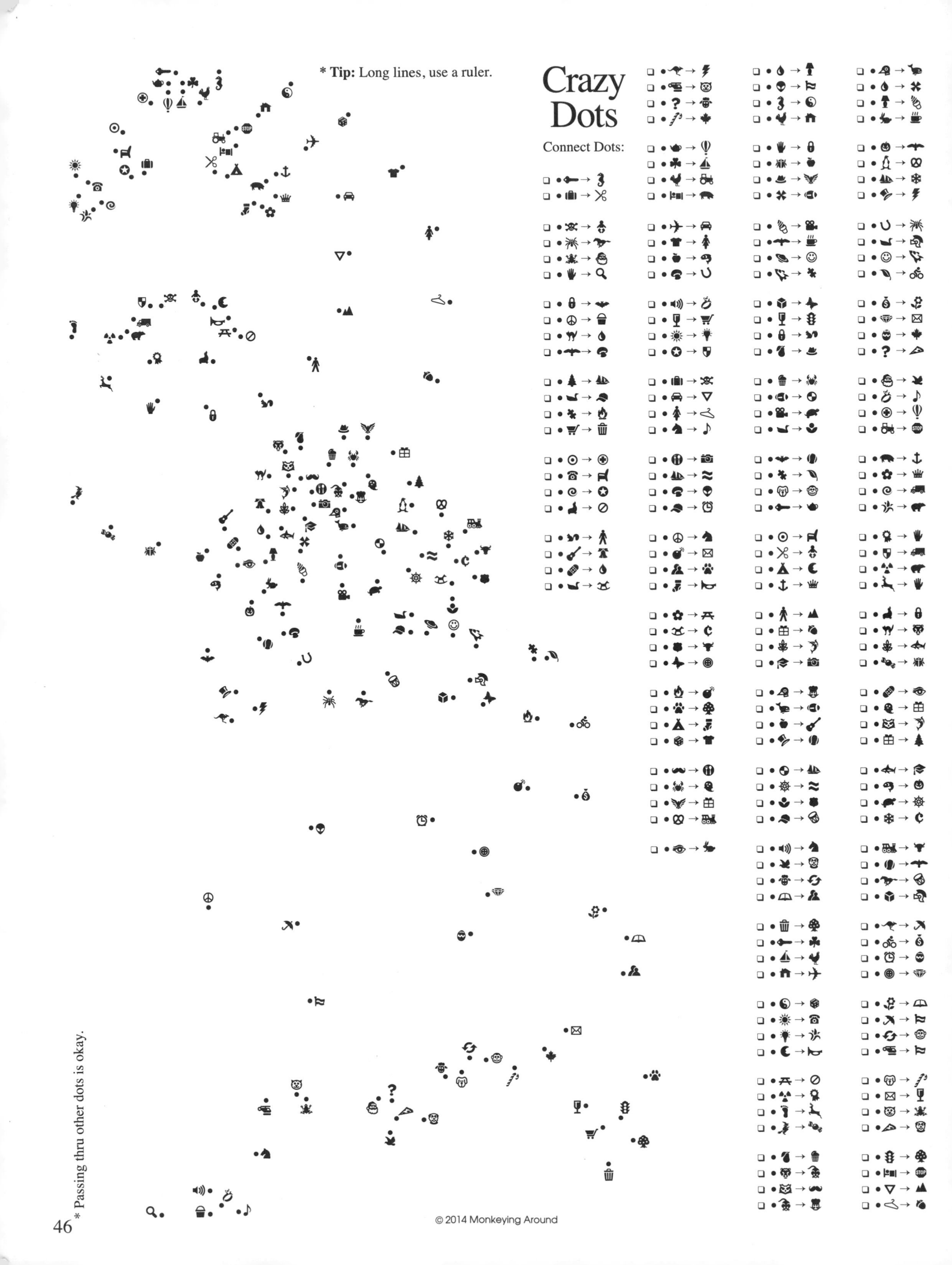
* Tip: Long lines, use a ruler.
Crazy Dots
Connect Dots:
* Passing thru other dots is okay.
© 2014 Monkeying Around